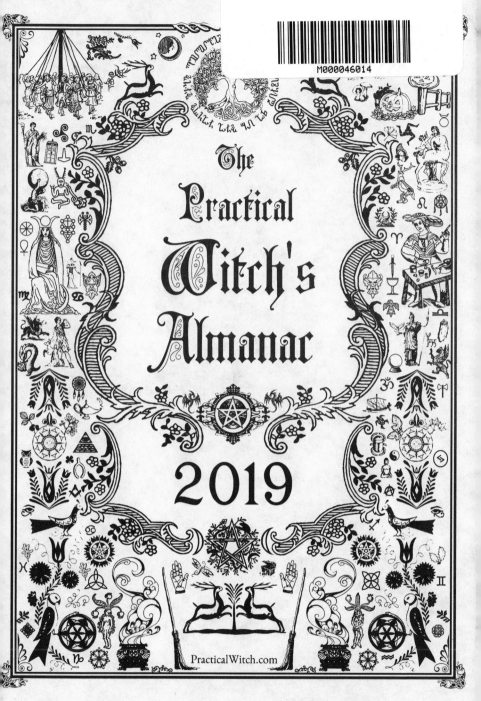

The
Practical
Witch's
Almanac

2019

PracticalWitch.com

Expanding Horizons

Volume XXII

The Practical Witch's Almanac

2019

PracticalWitch.com

Friday Gladheart

PRACTICAL WITCH'S ALMANAC
Expanding Horizons

This edition © Microcosm Publishing, 2019
First published September, 2019
ISBN 978-1-62106-731-3
This is Microcosm #411

2019 / 22st EDITION

For a catalog, write or visit:
Microcosm Publishing
2752 N Williams Ave.
Portland, OR 97227
(503)799-2698
Microcosm.Pub

To join the ranks of high-class stores that feature Microcosm titles, talk to your rep: In the U.S. **Como** (Atlantic), **Fujii** (Midwest), **Book Travelers West** (Pacific), **Turnaround** in Europe, **Manda/UTP** in Canada, **New South** in Australia, and **GPS** in Asia, India, Africa, and South America.

If you bought this on Amazon, I'm so sorry because you could have gotten it cheaper and supported a small, independent publisher at **Microcosm.Pub**

Global labor conditions are bad, and our roots in industrial Cleveland in the 70s and 80s made us appreciate the need to treat workers right. Therefore, our books are MADE IN THE USA and printed on post-consumer paper.

MICROCOSM · PUBLISHING

Microcosm Publishing is Portland's most diversified publishing house and distributor with a focus on the colorful, authentic, and empowering. Our books and zines have put your power in your hands since 1996, equipping readers to make positive changes in their lives and in the world around them. Microcosm emphasizes skill-building, showing hidden histories, and fostering creativity through challenging conventional publishing wisdom with books and bookettes about DIY skills, food, bicycling, gender, self-care, and social justice. What was once a distro and record label was started by Joe Biel in his bedroom and has become among the oldest independent publishing houses in Portland, OR. We are a politically moderate, centrist publisher in a world that has inched to the right for the past 80 years.

Thank You!

This is a special thanks to **you** for choosing the Practical Witch's Almanac and for supporting a great independent publisher. Visit Microcosm.Pub for more amazing titles. To give back to Mother Earth a tree is planted for every printed copy sold. Trees are planted at a sanctuary near the location pinned below.

Convert times provided in your almanac to other time zones using the map below or by visiting PracticalWitch.com. While there, check out the bonuses and free gifts.

Data Provided in Central Time

Daylight Savings Time included Mar. 10 - Nov. 3

Pacific
-2 Hours

Mountain
-1 Hour

Central/Almanac Time

Atlantic
+2 Hours

Eastern
+1 Hour

Hawaii
Aleutian
-4 Hours

Alaska
-3 Hours

Your Almanac is fitted to
W 093º 21', N 34° 35'

Welcome to the 22ⁿᵈ Edition: Expanding Horizons

This year's theme is **Expanding Horizons.** Practical Witches are a strong and fearless lot, welcoming adventure and new opportunities. Your almanac gives you several ways to expand your horizons and try new things.

Articles, recipes, spells, and DIY projects enhance your daily life and enrich your spirit. The precise calculations for astrological events keep you looking up, and the addition of holidays of diverse cultures and spiritual traditions help you live in harmony with those around you. Major Pagan festivals are noted this year to help you meet new people, and new birthdays are included of individuals who have worked toward equality, civil rights, or expanding all of our horizons. Intuitive psychic insights can be found at the bottom of your weekly planner pages and give you an edge on your week. Planner pages now have a blank box for you to add extra notes.

Along with your almanac comes full access to your Members Area of PracticalWitch.com. Decipher the hidden code in Theban Script at the back of your almanac to log in to the website. Every month you will find new gifts and bonuses:]

- Download Full-Size Monthly Wall Calendar Pages
- Discover Printable Tarot Decks & Zener Cards
- Access More Recipes, Spells & Articles
- Convert Any Time to Your Local Time Zone
- Get Coupons, Horoscopes, Tarot Readings & Free Gifts
- Import Your Almanac to Your Digital Calendar: iCal & Google

The Earth provides us with a beautiful dance of seasons and cycles, waltzing in the planetary ballroom of our galaxy. Your almanac is your personal companion, inviting you to join in on that dance every day, connect with your magic and with the wonders of nature. May you find many bright blessings this year!

Almanac Index

January

Week	Mo	Tu	We	Th	Fr	Sa	Su
1		1	2	3	4	5	6
2	7	8	9	10	11	12	13
3	14	15	16	17	18	19	20
4	21	22	23	24	25	26	27
5	28	29	30	31			

5:● 14:◐ 21:○ 27:◑

February

Week	Mo	Tu	We	Th	Fr	Sa	Su
5					1	**A**	**C**
6	4	5	6	7	8	9	10
7	11	12	13	14	15	16	17
8	18	19	20	21	22	23	24
9	25	26	27	28			

4:● 12:◐ 19:○ 26:◑

March

Week	Mo	Tu	We	Th	Fr	Sa	Su
9					1	2	3
10	4	5	6	7	8	9	10
11	11	12	13	14	15	16	17
12	18	19	**B**	21	22	23	24
13	25	26	27	28	29	30	31

6:● 14:◐ 20:○ 28:◑

April

Week	Mo	Tu	We	Th	Fr	Sa	Su
14	1	2	3	4	5	6	7
15	8	9	10	11	12	13	14
16	15	16	17	18	19	20	21
17	22	23	24	25	26	27	28
18	29	30					

5:● 12:◐ 19:○ 26:◑

May

Week	Mo	Tu	We	Th	Fr	Sa	Su
18		**A**	2	3	4	**C**	
19	6	7	8	9	10	11	12
20	13	14	15	16	17	18	19
21	20	21	22	23	24	25	26
22	27	28	29	30	31		

4:● 11:◐ 18:○ 26:◑

June

Week	Mo	Tu	We	Th	Fr	Sa	Su
22						1	2
23	3	4	5	6	7	8	9
24	10	11	12	13	14	15	16
25	17	18	19	20	**B**	22	23
26	24	25	26	27	28	29	30

3:● 10:◐ 17:○ 25:◑

Almanac Use & Major Symbols

Your planner pages are marked with the week number
that corresponds to the left column of the mini-calendars above.
Herbalism, gardening, and other symbols are on the next pages.

● New   ◐ 1ˢᵗ Quarter   ○ Full   ◑ 3ʳᵈ/Last Quarter

 Meteor Shower   Mercury Retrograde   Mercury Direct

 Solar Eclipse   Lunar Eclipse

Almanac Index

July

Week	Mo	Tu	We	Th	Fr	Sa	Su
27	1	2	3	4	5	6	7
28	8	9	10	11	12	13	14
29	15	16	17	18	19	20	21
30	22	23	24	25	26	27	28
31	29	30	31				

2:● 9:◑ 16:○ 24:◐ 31:●

August

Week	Mo	Tu	We	Th	Fr	Sa	Su
31				**A**	2	3	4
32	5	6	**C**	8	9	10	11
33	12	13	14	15	16	17	18
34	19	20	21	22	23	24	25
35	26	27	28	29	30	31	

7:◑ 15:○ 23:◐ 30:●

September

Week	Mo	Tu	We	Th	Fr	Sa	Su
35							1
36	2	3	4	5	6	7	8
37	9	10	11	12	13	14	15
38	16	17	18	19	20	21	22
39	**B**	24	25	26	27	28	29
40	30						

5:◑ 14:○ 21:◐ 28:●

October

Week	Mo	Tu	We	Th	Fr	Sa	Su
40		1	2	3	4	5	6
41	7	8	9	10	11	12	13
42	14	15	16	17	18	19	20
43	21	22	23	24	25	26	27
44	28	29	30	31			

5:◑ 13:○ 21:◐ 27:●

November

Week	Mo	Tu	We	Th	Fr	Sa	Su
44				**A**	2	3	
45	4	5	6	**C**	8	9	10
46	11	12	13	14	15	16	17
47	18	19	20	21	22	23	24
48	25	26	27	28	29	30	

4:◐ 12:○ 19:◐ 26:●

December

Week	Mo	Tu	We	Th	Fr	Sa	Su
48							1
49	2	3	4	5	6	7	8
50	9	10	11	12	13	14	15
51	16	17	18	19	20	**B**	22
52	23	24	25	26	27	28	29
01	30	31					

4:◐ 12:○ 18:◐ 26:●

Sabbats Above & Planner Page Symbols

A.   B.   C.

A. Traditional 'greater' Sabbats. Most celebrations begin the prior Eve, and may continue to the exact cross-quarter.

B. Equinox and Solstice Sabbats are precise astronomical dates.

C. Exact cross-quarter Sabbats are spacially calculated through interpolating the midway points between the Solstices and Equinoxes measured in degrees along the ecliptic.

Sun & Moon Distances

Perihelion: When the Earth is closest to the Sun for the year.

Aphelion: When the Earth is farthest from the Sun for 2019.

 Apogee: The Moon is farthest from the Earth in it's elliptical orbit and may appear smaller.

 Perigee: The Moon is close to the Earth and will appear 12% - 14% larger than the Moon at apogee.

When a Full Moon coincides with perigee, it is often called a "Supermoon". A moon at perigee will influence oceanic tides (tides may be up to 30% higher) and magical workings.

Apogee and perigee are marked for every lunar cycle of 24 to 28 days, known as an anomalistic month. The closest perigee and farthest apogee for 2019 are also marked in your planner pages.

What are You Fishing For?

While spending hundreds of hours on calculations for your almanac, it becomes clear that there are best times to engage in certain activities. Lunar, tidal, and weather forces coincide with subtle energies to increase the likelihood of success in many endeavors. The dates below are good times to attract or draw toward you: **prosperity, opportunities, fertility, strength, and good luck.** These are also good days for **travel, finding lost objects, hunting, and fishing,** and finding magical or spiritual **tools** (eg. wands) will be easier.

January 6–20	May 5–17	September 2–13, 29
February 5–18	June 4–16	October 2–12, 28, 29
March 7–19	July 3–15, 30	November 2–11, 27–29
April 6–18	August 2–14, 30	December 2–11, 27–30

Almanac Moon Signs

The primary lunar energy we perceive as the moon transits through each sign of the zodiac.

♈ **Aries:** Short-term objectives and challenges. Be quick.

♉ **Taurus:** Long-term objectives for solid foundations.

♊ **Gemini:** Thoughts and communication objectives.

♋ **Cancer:** Home, security, comfort and family.

♌ **Leo:** Creativity, taking risks, charisma and charity.

♍ **Virgo:** Details, routines, calculated tasks.

♎ **Libra:** Connections, cooperation, harmonious objectives

♏ **Scorpio:** Accounting for self and closing old accounts.

♐ **Sagittarius:** Adventures, expanding objectives.

♑ **Capricorn:** Long-term objectives, practical goals.

♒ **Aquarius:** Connections, new group objectives.

♓ **Pisces:** Magical and spiritual objectives, creativity.

Lunar Gardening & Workcunning

Witches and permaculturist share an understanding that the practice of producing food, medicines, and energy must be performed sustainably. Both also share the objectives of working harmoniously with the resources, features, and patterns all around us. Gardening "by the Moon" helps to achieve these goals, and Witches enjoy the added energy of the appropriate moon phase when working with herbs.

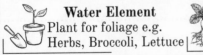

Water Element
Plant for foliage e.g. Herbs, Broccoli, Lettuce

Earth Element
Store foods. Plant for roots e.g. Mandrake, Garlic, Beets

Fire Element
Plant or harvest fruits and seeds e.g. Berries

Air Element
Harvest herbs and leaves for food, potions, medicine

Days unmarked are good for weeding, mowing, potion making.
Biodynamic Gardeners: Moon Opposition Saturn is noted.

Table of Contents

Happiness, Energy & Balance Spell

We all have many desires and needs, but instead of being consumer-minded there is a much more successful way to use personal power to achieve happiness, well-being, optimism, increased energy, mental balance, better tolerance, reduced frustration, and increased self-confidence. You can become more attuned and have better control over your empathy by using this gratitude spell.

This spell works through valid psychological techniques as well as spiritual and magical truths. Modern spells such as this work far better than the "bat wings and boiled bones" of the past. Give it a shot, you'll be grateful!

Timing Your Spell: For this spell, you will be creating a powerfully charged talisman you can carry with you. Begin your spell on the First Quarter Moon of the month and complete it on the Full Moon. You can perform this spell any time the moon is waxing, but if you were to do it in January, you would begin on the 14th and end on the 21st. The effects of this spell will be evident to most practitioners after just a few days, but continued focus of your *will* for at least a week results in exponential success.

Select a Talisman: A stone, crystal or piece of jewelry that is absorptive or receptive is a great item to make into a talisman. Your favorite pentacle or triquetra necklace, a clear quartz crystal, a tumble-polished rose quartz, lapis lazuli, moonstone or smooth landscaping rock will all do nicely. The object you choose should be easy for you to carry for the week it takes to complete your spell. Once your talisman is imbued with power, holding it will increase your happiness and energy while helping you put stressful situations into an optimistic perspective for better problem-solving.

Charging Your Talisman: The directions for this working are shockingly simple. Every day, hold the object you have chosen and

Monday 31

← Moon in Scorpio

Tuesday 1

Federal Holiday: New Year's Day

Wednesday 2

Perihelion: 11:19pm Earth is
closest to the Sun in orbit.
Moon enters Sagittarius 2:59am

Thursday 3

Quadrantids

Friday 4

Quadrantids

Jason Mankey's Birthday
Doreen Valiente's Birthday
Moon enters Capricorn 12:55pm
Isaac Newton's Birthday 1643
World Braille Day: ⠠ ⠶⠅ ⠒

Saturday 5

● 7:29pm
7:41pm Partial: not visible

Sunday 6

Venus in East before Sunrise
Twi: 6:54am-Rise: 7:22am
Set: 5:17pm-Twi: 5:45pm

Fresh beginnings on a tight budget.

focus on one thing that you are grateful for. Of course, you may repeat the exercise throughout the day whenever you think of something for which you are grateful. If you carry the talisman in your pocket while you are in public, just touch it while you focus. Close your eyes and *feel* the gratitude you have and send it through your hand into the talisman. Truly *feel* your thankfulness and gratitude. Do not allow guilt or a sense of indebtedness creep into your thoughts and emotions. This isn't about owing back, it's about true appreciation, acknowledging and accepting your blessings. Remember to hold your talisman and focus at least once every day.

You may speak words of power or a prayer of thanks to your chosen God(s) or Goddess(es) at the end of your energy projection, but sometimes the deep sense of gratitude may overwhelm you to the point that there are no words to express it. You may just end the focusing session with "so mote it be".

There is always something to be grateful for. We are living in such an amazing society, much akin to being at the peak of the Roman empire. Most of us reading this live in what many would consider a state of privilege known in earlier times only to royalty. We have access to communication never before seen, exotic fruits such as bananas from far away lands, education that allows us a vast majority of us to be able to read, and transportation that will carry us farther in one day than most humans of the past had traveled in their lifetimes. Even "negative" situations can be cause for thanks. Sometimes terrible situations lead us to the most amazing opportunities.

On the last day of your focusing and projecting exercises, the energy of the Full Moon reflects the fullness of your gratitude. Carry your talisman with you whenever you need a spiritual lift. As the year progresses, you may wish to boost its energy of your talisman by repeating your focus during any waxing moon phase.

Monday 7

Moon enters Aquarius 12:46am
International Programmer's Day

Tuesday 8

10:28pm

Wednesday 9

Moon enters Pisces 1:44pm

Thursday 10

Friday 11

Saturday 12

Moon enters Aries 2:18am

Sunday 13

Twi: 6:54am-Rise: 7:21am
Set: 5:23pm-Twi: 5:51pm

Take care of your mode of transportation.

Cakes & Ale

Witches often conclude gatherings and rituals with cakes and ale. This varies from cookies and milk to crab puffs and wine. The most popular recipe for modern Sabbat cakes allows for vegan and gluten-free options. It was created by one of our almanac authors in 1985 and is known as PaganPath Sabbat Cakes.

In a large bowl or cauldron thoroughly mix:

1 ½ cups unbleached organic Flour*
⅓-½ cup organic Cocoa Powder   ½ tsp. sea salt
1 tsp. Baking Soda   1 cup Sugar

In a separate bowl or cauldron whisk:

1 cup very strong, cold Coffee, Expresso, or dark carbonated Soda such as cola, root beer or "pepper" flavors.
½ tsp. ground Cloves   1 tsp. Cinnamon
2 tsp. Vanilla Extract   1 Egg*

Spray muffin tins with non-stick spray or use silicone cupcake pans. Use ⅓ cocoa unless you like dark chocolate, then use ½ cup. Pour the liquid ingredients into the dry ingredients and combine well. Divide the batter evenly into muffin cups and bake at 350°F for about 25 minutes, or until a toothpick inserted into the center of a cupcake comes out clean.

Frost as desired, or try sprinkling powdered sugar from a sifter over the cake. Use stencils to make sugar designs for your celebration, or just drizzle melted milk chocolate over the tops.

Makes 12 Cupcakes   tsp. = Teaspoon
* Gluten-free all-purpose baking mix may be used instead of flour.
* Egg may be omitted if desired.

Monday 14

◐ 12:47am
Moon enters Taurus 12:32pm

Tuesday 15

Wednesday 16

Moon enters Gemini 7:01pm

Thursday 17

Friday 18

Moon enters Cancer 9:44pm

Saturday 19

☾ Sunday 20

11:17pm
Total, visible

Cold
○ 11:17pm Supermoon!
Moon enters Leo 9:55pm
Twi: 6:52am-Rise: 7:19am
Set: 5:30pm-Twi: 5:57pm
3:00am Sun enters Aquarius

Communication is easier, good messages arrive.

Plants that Stay Warm

You maintain a body temperature of around 37 °C (98.6 °F) as do many warm-blooded animals. But there are some remarkable plants that also have thermoregulation. The best example is the Sacred Lotus (Nelumbo nucifera) which can produce its own heat.

This lotus is also known as *Padma* and it plays an important role in Buddhism, Hinduism, and Jainism. The flowers maintain a temperature around 30–35 °C (86–95 °F). There are other magical plants that can produce heat.

Some of these thermogenic plants have the ability to maintain the temperature of certain plant parts, especially the center of their flowers, up to 45 °C (113 °F). The heat produced may help protect them from tissue damage due to freezing temperatures.

These extraordinary plants grow all over the world. Eastern Skunk Cabbage is also thermogenic and can be found from Quebec and Nova Scotia all the way to Minnesota, North and South Carolina and Tennessee (where it is endangered and protected).

Thermogenic plants are in ancient groups of seed plants including paleoherbs like some of the Nymphaeaceae (Water Lily) family and the Aristolochiaceae (Birthwort family). There are other plant families that have members with thermogenic abilities such as Arecaceae (Palms), Araceae (Arum Lilies or Aroids), Nelumbonaceae (True Lotuses), Aristolochiaceae (Dutchman's Pipe), Annonaceae (Custard Apples) and Cyclanthaceae (Panama Hat Palms).

Om Mani Pädme Hum

Monday 21

1:59pm
World Religions Day
Fed: Martin Luther King, Jr. Day

Tuesday 22

Venus & Jupiter together in the East
before Sunrise: Luck in Love all day
Moon enters Virgo 9:22pm

Wednesday 23

Thursday 24

Moon enters Libra 10:03pm

Friday 25

Virginia Wolf's Birthday

Saturday 26

Ellen DeGeneres's Birthday

Sunday 27

World Holocaust Victim's
Remembrance Day

◑3:12pm
Moon enters Scorpio 1:31am
Twi: 6:49am-Rise: 7:16am
Set: 5:37pm-Twi: 6:04pm

You know what is best; You are your own authority figure.

Translating Roman Numerals

Have you ever wondered about those letters you see on major arcana tarot cards? They are *Roman Numerals* and even if you don't like math, you can read them by using this reference guide.

When a letter appears twice it is doubled. For example, II is two and XX is twenty. The same goes for tripling, III is three and XXX is thirty. If a letter with a lower value is to the <u>left</u> of a letter with a greater value, you <u>subtract</u> the lower from the greater.

$$IV = 5 \ (V) \text{ minus } 1 \ (I) = 4$$
$$IX = 10 \ (X) \text{ minus } 1 \ (I) = 9$$
$$CD = 500 \ (D) - 100 \ (C) = 400$$

When a letter of lower value is on the <u>right</u> of a letter with greater value, you <u>add</u> the lower to the greater.

$$VI = 5 \ (V) + 1 \ (I) = 6$$
$$XI = 10 \ (X) + 1 \ (I) = 11$$
$$DC = 500 \ (D) + 100 \ (C) = 600$$

A line appearing over a letter indicates that you should multiply the number by a thousand such as $\overline{V}$ in the chart below.

1	I	9	IX	17	XVII	70	LXX	600	DC
2	II	10	X	18	XVIII	80	LXXX	700	DCC
3	III	11	XI	19	XIX	90	XC	800	DCCC
4	IV	12	XII	20	XX	100	C	900	CM
5	V	13	XIII	30	XXX	200	CC	1000	M
6	VI	14	XIV	40	XL	300	CCC	2000	MM
7	VII	15	XV	50	L	400	CD	3000	MMM
8	VIII	16	XVI	60	LX	500	D	5000	$\overline{V}$

Monday 28	Tuesday 29
	Moon enters Sagittarius 8:33am Oprah Winfrey's Birthday
Wednesday 30	**Thursday 31**
Z. Budapest's Birthday	
Friday 1	**Saturday 2** 9:01pm
National Freedom Day Moon in Capricorn	
Sunday 3	
Twi: 6:45am-Rise: 7:11am Set: 5:44pm-Twi: 6:11pm Moon enters Aquarius 7:04am Gertrude Stein's Birthday	

Love yourself as you wish others to.

The Chinese Year of the Pig

This is the year of the Pig, in the element of Earth. The energy of the year and the traits of those born in this year are said to be influenced by the spirit of the pig.

Pig is all about generosity, compassion, and communication. Pig does not overlook details and has great concentration. Matters of time and goal-oriented plans come easily to Pig. Challenges and responsibilities are handled carefully and thoughtfully. However, Pig is sometimes lazy and is not suspicious so can be fooled easily.

In China, celebrations of the new year begin on January 28th and last until New Year's eve on the 4th. The next day is the official New Year and celebrations of the Spring Festival continue to February 29th. During the Spring Festival, when the moon is 15 days old, is the Lantern Festival. Celebrations begin early on February 16th, but the main event is on February 19th.

This extraordinary fire festival is simply **awe**some. Legendary origin stories of the Lantern Festival center around the themes of protection, especially from fire. Beautiful paper lanterns are created meticulously by hand. Thousands of red lanterns fill the sky while elaborate paper lantern dragons and other creatures adorn the ground. This year look for Pig lanterns!

An interesting bit of magic is performed during the Spring Festival. Although losing popularity in modern cities, some still honor Son-In-Law Day. On the second day of the Chinese New Year, newly married couples bring gifts (Red Envelopes) and visit their mother-in-law's home. The new husband is the honored guest in his mother-in-law house, and the wife's parents bestow two lotus lanterns upon the young couple. One lantern is red, the other white.

When the young couple returns home after lunch, usually around 3pm, they light the lotus lamps in the bedroom. If the white lotus burns out first they will have a male son, if the red burns out first their next child will be female.

Monday 4

●3:05pm
Chinese New Year 豬
Year of the Brown Earth Pig

Tuesday 5

Farthest for 2019 at 3:28am

Moon enters Pisces 8:02pm

Wednesday 6

Thursday 7

Friday 8

Moon enters Aries 8:35am

Saturday 9

Sunday 10

Moon enters Taurus 7:29pm
Twi: 6:39am-Rise: 7:05am
Set: 5:51pm-Twi: 6:17pm

Squash gossip & jealousy with love & kindness. Lucky Pig Year #s: 2, 5, 8

Dragon's Blood

Dragon's Blood (DB) is a red resin that when ground, looks a bit like dried blood. It is obtained from a variety of plant species, but the most popular DB comes from the Daemonorops palm. Practical Witches use DB as an antioxidant, styptic, and astringent in balms and lotions while giving these potions a magical power boost. You can use it to add power and "oomph" to spells or to make an ink for inscribing tools, talismans, and books of shadows with magical sigils and seals. DB increases the potency of magical workings, aids in returning lost love, and has powerful protection properties as mentioned above. Primarily, it is used for **purification and increasing energy psychically, magically and spiritually**. It is also said to enhance health, virility and to cure impotency. A very good use of the resin is to add it to incense mixtures or 'mojo bags' to enhance their energy and aid in blending the other ingredients.

It is attributed to the Root and Sacral Chakras, and workings for **love, sexuality, survival, power, reproduction, solidity, potency, grounding, protection, and manifestation** are the focus of most magical uses. For most spells, its use if for power and protection, especially protection from psychic predators.

Because it is a brittle resin similar to copal or frankincense, it can be processed very much like these familiar resins. However, most DB incense does not actually contain the resin. The scent of burning dragon's blood varies, and not every DB has a good smoke fragrance. However, you can add a small amount to your favorite incense to add the magical properties of DB.

Place your favorite incense into a bag or container with finely ground DB. Gently turn the container until the incense has been coated with the powder. You can take this a step further by making your own incense for use on charcoals. You will find several incense recipes in your almanac, some of which include dragon's blood.

Monday 11

Tuesday 12

◑ 4:27pm

Wednesday 13

Thursday 14

Moon enters Gemini 3:32am
World Radio Day

Valentine's Day

Friday 15

Saturday 16

Galileo Day
Moon enters Cancer 8:03am
Susan B, Anthony's Birthday
Buddhism: Nirvana Day
PantheaCon Begins ⟶

Moon Opposition Saturn

Sunday 17

* PantheaCon is a large Pagan
conference in San Jose, CA

Moon enters Leo 9:21am
Twi: 6:32am-Rise: 6:58am
Set: 5:58pm-Twi: 6:24pm

Practice patience in your communications.

The Simpler's Method

Long ago, a "simpler" was an herbalist, healer, or a person who practiced wortcunning. A traditional method of measurement for herbal formulas is known as the *Simpler's Method*. This type of measurement is very easy to understand and memorize and allows great flexibility in recipe quantities.

Recipe ingredients are measured in *Parts*. Parts may be volume such as 1 teaspoon, or weight such as 1 gram. For precision, a recipe must use only one, either a volume part or a weight part. Most incense recipes use volume, and essential oil or medicinal recipes use weight. Parts are based on ratios, and a part can be any size or weight you prefer.

As an example, consider the "simple syrup" used as an ingredient in drinks, herbal remedies, and cocktails. The standard recipe uses volume and is 1 part sugar to 1 part water. If you wish to make a gallon of syrup, you would use ½ gallon sugar and ½ gallon water. To make a cup of syrup, you would use a ½ cup measuring cup to measure out each part.

Incense recipes are nearly always provided parts by volume. Note the ratios for the following recipe, and how the traditional Simpler's Method can be used to make as much or little as desired.

Purification & Cleansing Incense

Parts (P) by volume, equal size resin pieces, sand to dry lentil size.

4P White Copal	4 teaspoons	4 Tablespoons	4 Cups
4P Gum Mastic	4 teaspoons	4 Tablespoons	4 Cups
1P Dragon's Blood	1 teaspoon	1 Tablespoon	1 Cup
Total Quantities	3 Tablespoons	Just over ½ Cup	Just over a ½ Gallon jar

Monday 18

Sun enters Pisces 5:04pm
Federal: Presidents' Day
Last day of PantheaCon

Tuesday 19

Lantern Festival →
Closest for 2019 at 3:02 am
Moon enters Virgo 8:47am
"Supermoon" ◯ 9:55am
Nicolaus Copernicus's Birthday

Wednesday 20

Thursday 21

Moon enters Libra 8:18am
Barbara Jordan's Birthday

Friday 22

Saturday 23

Moon enters Scorpio 9:57am

Sunday 24

Twi: 6:25am-Rise: 6:50am
Set: 6:04pm-Twi: 6:30pm

A cold week brings a cool head and introspection.

Incense Recipes

All incense recipes in your almanac are in parts by volume. See The Simpler's Method article for help with these measurements. Do not use fresh herbs, dry them first. Crushed leaves are the size sold in groceries when you buy basil, "Italian" spice or oregano. This type of magical and ritual incense should be used on a special incense charcoal disk. These disks are sold in ten-pack tubes and are safe for indoor use. *Do not use grilling/BBQ charcoals indoors!*

Passion & Sensuality:

1 part ground Cloves
1 part ground Dragon's Blood resin
6 parts Sandalwood powder
1 part ground fragrant Amber*

* Use the "amber resin perfume", sometimes sold as solid amber incense resin. This is a natural blend of resins used to impart a sweet, heart-opening fragrance.

Lucky Mojo #9

1 part ground Cinnamon
1 part ground Cloves
1 part Ginger Root powder
1 part crushed Patchouli leaves
1 part crushed Basil leaves
1 part crushed Five-Finger Grass (Cinquefoil)
3 parts Frankincense (tears about dry lentil size)
6 parts Sandalwood powder

Use this incense to attract opportunities, prosperity, abundance, success, and good luck. A practical substitute for the first three ingredients is pumpkin-spice blend available at grocery stores.

Monday 25

Moon enters Sagittarius 3:20pm
Spring whispers in the breeze.

Tuesday 26

◐ 5:29am

Wednesday 27

Thursday 28

Moon enters Capricorn 12:49am

Friday 1

Saturday 2

Moon enters Aquarius 1:07pm

March is Women's History Month

Sunday 3

National Academy of
Sciences Founded 1863
Twi: 6:16am-Rise: 6:42am
Set: 6:11pm-Twi: 6:36pm

Look deeply to find what You really want.

Extracted Oils for Practical Witches

Essential oils (EO) are steam distilled from plants. They are an extremely concentrated form of the plant, and should seldom be used straight from the bottle. Genuine EO do not contain synthetic ingredients and are not altered or diluted.

A *few* companies alter their essential oils, providing such justifications as that they do it for public safety, or they dilute in order to "standardize" their products. These may be legitimate claims, but practical Witches are a smart and savvy lot, and we can dilute our essential oils all by ourselves.

Attars (AT) are a type of perfume made with EO in a base. The base oil is usually an EO such as sandalwood or aloeswood. The AT is then aged for up to ten years. A tradition in India dating back over 5,000 years is to give guest to your home a small vial of AT. They are used in magic and medicine to this day, often as an aphrodisiac, to uplift the mood, or to remove evil spirits.

Some fragrances are too delicate to be extracted with steam as such as jasmine, violet, and narcissus. Solvent extraction is often used for these fragile scents. The resulting extract is known as an absolute (AB) and it is extremely high in fragrance concentration. The aroma of an AB is more closely akin to the original plant material than most essential oils.

A solvent such as hexane, ether, or alcohol is forced through the plant material. The solvent is then removed from the extracted material and recovered for re-use. The remaining plant material of this "first draw" is known as a *concrete*. Concrete is then flushed with alcohol to remove excess plant waxes and chlorophyll, yielding an absolute. The U.S. Pharmacopeia sets limits on residual solvents, and most absolutes on the market fall well within these standards. It is in a company's best interest to recover as much of their expensive solvents as possible.

continued next week. . .

Monday 4	Tuesday 5 ♀ Retro 12:18pm
5:26am	Moon enters Pisces 2:11am
Wednesday 6	Thursday 7
● 10:05am Ash Wednesday-Christian Lent begins	Moon enters Aries 2:28pm
Friday 8	Saturday 9
International Women's Day	
Sunday 10 Daylight Savings Time Begins 2:00am Harriet Tubman's Birthday Moon enters Taurus 1:10am Twi: 7:07am-Rise: 7:32am Set: 7:17pm-Twi: 7:42pm	

Good judgment brings reconciliation.

. . .continued from last week.

Absolutes (AB) are usually extracted without the use of additional heat that would destroy delicate chemicals in the plants. But there is another form of extraction that never uses heat.

With the CO2 method, carbon dioxide is forced through the plant material. Like AB, this method allows for a more a more complete extraction of components that would be destroyed by steam heat or are not water soluble.

Perfume oils or Fragrance oils (FO) are synthetic. These lab creations can be both a blessing and a bane. The National Academy of Sciences reported that 95% of chemicals used in synthetic fragrances are derived from petrochemicals. The list of chemicals includes aldehydes and benzene derivatives. FO manufacturers are not required to disclose their ingredients under the "trade secret" status. A label listing "artificial fragrance" may contain dozens of potential allergens, mutagens, hormone disruptors, and other toxins.

There are also "nature identical" synthetic fragrances. These are extremely pure, high-quality chemicals that are identical to those extracted from plants. They are very helpful when natural ingredients are in short supply, especially from endangered plants or crop failures. Nature identical FO enable more people to share the experiences of rare, precious and prohibitively expensive scents.

There is no respected organization or governmental agency that formally approves grading standards used in the EO industry. **Terms such as therapeutic grade, aromatherapy grade, and medicinal grade are purely hype and marketing maneuvers.**

Some dealers wish to convey the quality of their oils to differentiate them from other brands that contain adulterants. Using meaningless terms does not increase their validity. Instead, insist upon a source origin (state, country) and get Certificates of Analysis and/or Gas Chromatography-Mass Spectrometric Analysis. EssentialOil.com clearly identifies their oils, and WindnWood.com is a trusted dealer for special orders over $200.

Monday 11

Douglas Adams's Birthday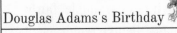

Tuesday 12

Moon enters Gemini 10:48am

Wednesday 13

Thursday 14

Moon enters
Cancer 4:50pm

◗ 5:28am
Albert Einstein's Birthday

Friday 15

Saturday 16

Moon enters Leo 7:57pm
Moon Opposition Saturn
Equilux at 30°N to 35°N

Sunday 17

Irish: St Patrick's Day
Twi: 6:58am-Rise: 7:23am
Set: 7:22pm-Twi: 7:47pm

Equilux is when day and night
appear equal depending on your
Latitude. This is usually a few
days before the Spring Equinox

Juggling projects brings rewards.

Magic Coconut Crisps

Coconuts are often used magically for protection and purification. They are also associated with water and the moon. Scientists are discovering the anti-microbial and anti-viral properties of coconut oil, and recent studies indicate that it may have anti-inflammatory properties in the body.

This recipe is a twist on the classic rice crispy treats. It is a favorite at Witchy gatherings because it is very simple, fairly inexpensive, and can accommodate many dietary requirements such as **gluten-free** and **vegan**. You can press the mixture into moulds to make wonderful shapes for rituals and celebrations, or use cookie cutters to cut shapes out of the pan before drizzling with chocolate. For Esbats, we like to shape them into round "moons" and coat the bottoms in chocolate or dip an edge to make moon phases.

3 Tablespoons Cold Pressed Organic Coconut Oil
1 (10 ounce) package Marshmallows (vegan are available)
1 Cup Coconut Flakes (sweetened or unsweetened)
6 Cups Crisp Rice Cereal (whole brown crisped rice is great)
6 ounces Chocolate Chips (semi-sweet, milk, your choice)

A) Spread coconut out in a 9" x 13" pan and toast in the oven at 325°F for 15 minutes. Stir coconut every 5 minutes. **B)** Heat coconut oil and marshmallows microwave on high for 2 minutes. Stir and heat again for one minute. Repeat until smooth. Stir in crisp rice and toasted coconut. **C)** Line the 9" x 13" pan with wax paper or coat it thoroughly with coconut oil. With an oiled spoon or spatula press the mixture into the pan making an even layer.
D) Place chocolate chips into a glass measuring cup and microwave for 30 seconds. Stir and microwave for 15 seconds. Repeat until smooth and drizzle over the mixture in the pan. Cut when cool.

Monday 18

Tuesday 19

2:47 pm

Wednesday 20

Equinox

4:58pm

Sun enters Aries 4:59pm
"Supermoon" ○ 8:44pm
Excellent day for magic!

Thursday 21

World Poetry Day
Hindu: Holi- Spring Festival

Friday 22

World Water Day
Moon enters Scorpio 9:17pm

Saturday 23

Sunday 24

Twi: 6:48am-Rise: 7:13am
Set: 7:28pm-Twi: 7:53pm

Be patient, bide your time and wait with grace.

The Impractical Grimoires

Grimoires, or "black books" are magical textbooks or instructional books that were very popular from the 1600s to 1800s. They came with fantastical titles such as the *Black Pullet*, *Red Dragon*, *Black Screech Owl*, *Key of Solomon*, or *Lemegeton*.

Although "grimoire" is a term used by some Witches interchangeably with Book of Shadows, the flavor of the two terms is quite different. Grimoires were highly influenced by Abrahamic religions, especially Judaism, and Christianity.

The Black Pullet (Poulet Noir) was most likely written in Rome in the late 18th century and contains instructions on the creation of magickal talismans, amulets, and jewelry - primarily rings. It was also published under the titles *Black Screech Owl* and *Treasure of the Old Man of the Pyramids* - both with only slight alterations. To add to the confusion, some practitioners refer to this grimoire as *The Hen that lays Golden Eggs* or *The Hen with the Golden Eggs* due to the instructions within the text for creating a "black pullet" which in turn will provide the practitioner with unlimited wealth.

Sources for the information in the various grimoires include Greek and Egyptian magical texts dating from 100 A.D. To 400 A.D. and also include Hebrew & Latin sources. These texts were used by ceremonial magicians to conjure and control demons, angels, spirits, etc. *Red Dragon* (also entitled *Grand Grimoire*) was published in 1822 but purports to date back to 1522. There is little evidence to substantiate this, as it was clearly written in the 1800s.

Grimoires contain elaborate rituals, most of which are not practical. Modern Witches have adopted small parts of some grimoires, and you will see echoes of the Key of Solomon and Lemegeton in Gardnerian and Alexandrian consecrations and quarter calls. This is probably from the founder of the Gardnerian Witchcraft Tradition (Gerald Gardner), who filled in missing gaps in his rituals to make them more usable and cohesive.

Monday 25

Moon enters Sagittarius 1:07am

Tuesday 26

Wednesday 27

◗ 11:11pm
Moon enters Capricorn 9:08am

Thursday 28

Direct
☿
8:59am

Friday 29

Moon enters Aquarius 8:46pm

Saturday 30

Sunday 31

Twi: 6:38am-Rise: 7:03am
Set: 7:33pm-Twi: 7:59pm

7:13pm
Cesar Chavez's Birthday

Keep your lips and purse strings tight.

Twilight, Tweens & The Golden Hour

Tweens are magical pockets that can be a place, a time period, or both. A physical tween might be the doorway to your home. It is not outside nor inside, it is be<u>tween</u> the two. A threshold tween holds a special energy and you will often forget what you were doing when you pass through a doorway. Have you ever wondered why you went into a room? A trick to retain your thoughts is to re-focus on your goal just before you pass through a threshold.

A tween in time feels similar to the hesitation of a pendulum on a clock when it swings all the way one direction, hesitates briefly in the tween and then swings in the other direction. Sabbats often mark such tweens in time, when the earth almost quivers with anticipation as she transitions from one season to the next. Your almanac gives you tween times for another special occurrence that happens twice every day, the "magical hour".

The magical hour is also known as twilight, but most almanacs do not specify if they are providing data for Nautical Twilight, Astronomical Twilight or Civil Twilight. For Witches, the practical choice is Civil Twilight because it coincides with a specific atmosphere and energy of tween-ness. This is the twilight that is a fortuitous time to meditate, do yoga, cast spells, pray, write, and take great pictures!

This magical hour is nearly the same as the "golden hour" used by photographers and filmmakers. The sun's rays are at a low angle and travel through more of the Earth's atmosphere scattering blue and violet wavelengths, so we see more orange and red.

The magical hour is noted as Twi in your almanac every week on the Sun's day (Sunday). Not long before sunrise, Civil Twilight (Twi) begins and then ends the moment the sun rises. At sunset, Twi begins again and ends at the time indicated in your almanac. The end time, like the beginning time, occurs when the geometric center of the sun is greater than 6° below the horizon.

Monday 1

April Fool's Day
Moon enters Pisces 9:48am

Tuesday 2

Wednesday 3

Moon entersAries 9:57pm

Thursday 4

Maya Angelou's Birthday

Friday 5

● 3:52am

Saturday 6

Moon enters Taurus 8:07am
Scottish American: Tartan Day

Sunday 7

Twi: 6:28am-Rise: 6:54am
Set: 7:39pm-Twi: 8:04pm

Introspection eases anticipation.

True Goals in Magic

Defining your True Goal (TG) is the most important step in getting what you want in everyday life as well as in magic. Before doing any energy work or spells, practical Witches ask difficult questions to find our TG. Once found, Witches face the challenge of gaining the TG while honoring their personal ethics and morality.

Creating a plan or designing a spell to reach one's goal is the next most important step mundanely and magically. But these plans are dependant upon the answers to the numerous difficult questions such as; *Do you really want money?* Or is your TG the vehicle you hope to purchase with that money? A TG must be very specific in order to avoid unnecessary harm or even disaster.

In addition to sussing out the TG, one must also consider how our actions will cause ripples like a stone thrown into the pool of the universe. Performing magic for rain may seem like a good idea, but perhaps we are not qualified to make such decisions. A spell to sway your boss into giving a promotion may allow a more qualified or needy person to be overlooked.

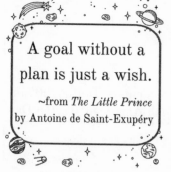

A goal without a plan is just a wish.

~from *The Little Prince* by Antoine de Saint-Exupéry

Deeper psychological questions are not overlooked during consideration of the TG. When you are in need of money, a prosperity spell may not do the trick if you have internal hesitations, or if the money is needed to feed an addiction. Working magic for love may not be successful if you do not love yourself or feel that you deserve love. Healing work must be approached holistically, focusing on curing the real problem or cause of a health issue rather than treating a symptom.

Reaching your true goal is much easier when you have honestly answered the difficult questions, and when you make a solid plan on both magical and mundane levels.

Monday 8

International Romani Day
Moon enters Gemini 4:15pm
Buddhism: Buddha's Birth

Tuesday 9

National Library
Workers' Day

Wednesday 10

Moon enters Cancer 10:32pm

Thursday 11

Mercury in the East low on
the horizon just before sunrise

Friday 12

◗ 2:07pm
Moon Opposition Saturn

Saturday 13

Moon enters Leo 2:50am

Sunday 14

Twi: 6:19am-Rise: 6:45am
Set: 7:44pm-Twi: 8:10pm

Someone you admired and trusted is loosing your support. Good riddance.

Hag Stones

In our modern use of the word, *hag* implies an ugly, aged woman. Not long ago this word had a different flavor. Haga is an Old English word meaning both *a marked off portion of woodland* and *hawthorn* (a magickal tree often associated with hedges).

Witches use the word hag in the older sense of the word, indicating a woman with prophetic and oracular powers, a seer, diviner, soothsayer, wise one, healer, hedge-priestess or one who dwells by the hedges. The name of hag stones is in reference to this older meaning of the word hag. Hag stones are used by Witches to increase **psychic powers** and **prophetic dreams**.

A hag stone is a stone with a hole worn through it by time and water. These are usually found near rivers and beaches, or sometimes in the foothills of mountain ranges. They are known to be powerful amulets for **protection and visions**. Called by many names, you will find legends about hag stones in nearly every corner of the world, particularly in Wales, Ireland, Northern Germany, Russia, and Scotland. The Druids were known to wear hag stones, and they have been found in Egyptian tombs.

When researching these wonderful tools, search for Adder Stones, Holey Stones, Holed Stones, Serpent's Eggs, Odin Stones, Witch Stones, Adderstanes, Gloine nah Druidh, or Glain Neidr.

It is said that you can look through the hole in such stones to **see the truth, see past glamour spells, and gain visions of the fairy realm**. They can be used for any type of magical work and make superior **protection** amulets. They **avert the Evil Eye, prevent nightmares and protect from baneful magic**. They are used for general **good luck** and to help **avoid misfortune**.

Monday 15

Moon enters Virgo 5:14am
Federal Tax Day

Tuesday 16

Margot Adler's
Birthday   5:04 pm

Wednesday 17

Moon enters Libra 6:22am

Thursday 18

CMA Beltane Festival Begins →

Friday 19

◯6:13am
Moon enters Scorpio 7:41am
Jewish: Passover begins

Saturday 20

Sun enters Taurus 3:56am

Sunday 21

→ CMA Beltane Festival ends |

Moon enters Sagittarius 11:00am
Christian: Easter
Twi: 6:10am-Rise: 6:36am
Set: 7:50pm-Twi: 8:16pm

CMA Beltane information:
The Council of Magickal Arts
holds a large Beltane festival
every year at SpiritHaven,
near Cistern, Texas

Good news comes this week. Check messages, phone calls, mail, email, etc.

Reading Tarot for Yourself

A common myth among new tarot readers is that you should not read the cards for yourself. This is simply not true, and reading your own cards is a great way to learn your own mind and the tarot. One must take care to not become reliant on the cards or obsessed with numerous daily readings, but that aside there are excellent reasons to read your own cards.

Gaining Direct Insight About Yourself: Who better to read for you than the person who knows you best? You! The tarot is a tool for you, not just for others.

Learning Tarot Applications In Life Situations: To become proficient in tarot, one must be very familiar with the cards, their meanings, and why they appear in layouts at different times in your life. To develop this familiarity, you will have to do a significant number of readings and gain follow-up feedback on how the cards you drew reflected real life. There is no better person to use as a guinea pig in this area than yourself.

Learning Objectivity: Although there are times that you may prefer an objective outside opinion about a reading for yourself, you should be training yourself to be an objective reader. Avoid letting your personal views get overly involved in a reading as they will significantly hinder the accuracy. When consulting a second opinion on readings for yourself, it is sometimes helpful to try another mode of divination first. Try scrying, runes or the I Ching.

The Moon

Shuffling Your Tarot: In order to ensure that your deck is properly mixed shuffle them <u>at least nine times</u> or place them all on a clean surface face down and mix them up by stirring them gently with your hands.

Monday 22

Lyrids

Tuesday 23

Lyrids

Order of the Garter Established
Moon enters Capricorn 5:50pm

Wednesday 24

Thursday 25

Friday 26

◗ 5:19pm
Moon enters Aquarius 4:28am

├─ 2 Day Native American Event: Gathering of Nations ─┤
Largest Pow Wow in North America in Albuquerque, NM

Saturday 27

Sunday 28

Moon enters Pisces 5:12pm

1:19 pm
Twi: 6:01am-Rise: 6:28am
Set: 7:56pm-Twi: 8:22pm

Healing and recovery from outside interference.

Elements, Elementals, Quarters & Corners

Ritual circles often begin with "calling the quarters" or "invoking the elements". The variety of ways that the forces of nature are invited (invoked) to the circle can cause confusion. As with nearly everything in the Craft, these forces are perceived differently by each individual. When you research these forces, let your intuition be your guide. Here are the basics to get you started.

The Elements: The classical elements as described by the Greek philosopher Empedocles; Earth, Air, Fire, Water. Aristotle proposed a fifth element, Æther (similar to Akashi in India). Each Element is associated with a cardinal direction (North, East, South, West) and these associations vary from coven to coven.

Elementals: Said to be lower-level being. Lower-level generally means that they are not Goddesses or Gods.

Watchtowers or Guardians: Devas called by names such as the Mighty Ones, Lords of the Watchtowers, and the Guardians of the Watchtowers. They rule over Elementals.

Corners: Usually refers to the four Cardinal points of the compass; North, East, South, West. Calling the Corners is a general term that indicates the part of casting a circle when the Elements, Elementals, and/or Watchtowers are called.

Calling the Quarters: This term can also indicate the invoking of any or all of the forces described here, and it is best to clarify with other practitioners before the circle begins.

The influence of grimoires from the 1600s to late 1800s is evident in the Elemental and Watchtower traditions. Most practitioners of Earth-based spiritual traditions focus on the Elements. The four classical Elements can represent emotions (Water), thoughts (Air), passion (Fire), and body (Earth). Contemplating different associations is an excellent meditation.

Monday 29

Tuesday 30

Wednesday 1

PaganPath.com's 22nd Anniversary

Moon enters Aries 5:24

Thursday 2

Jewish: Days of Remembrance
of the Victims of the Holocaust

Friday 3

World Press Freedom Day
Moon enters Taurus 3:18pm

Saturday 4

● 5:54am
Space Day
Star Wars Day
Keith Harring's Birthday

Sunday 5

1:58pm

Cinco de Mayo
Moon enters Gemini 10:40pm
Twi: 6:01am-Rise: 6:28am
Set: 7:56pm-Twi: 8:22pm

Hope is not lost. Frustration and restraints lift this week.

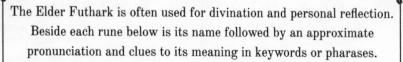

Runes

The Elder Futhark is often used for divination and personal reflection. Beside each rune below is its name followed by an approximate pronunciation and clues to its meaning in keywords or pharases.

Fehu "fay-who": Controlled power over wealth. Manifesting creative energy and power. Invest wisely to increase wealth.

Uruz "ooo-rooze" Vital strength, primal power, determination health, perseverance, manifestation, wisdom & lore.

Thurisaz "thoor-ee-saws" Thorn, protection, fence, barrier, enemy of baneful forces, defense, destruction, applied power.

Ansuz "awn-sooze" Breath, word/song (as in words of power or incantations), shaping power or sound, expression, communication.

Raidho "rye-though" Riding, wheel, journey and travel, quest, change, ritual, rhythm, movement, order, underworld.

Kenaz "kane-awze" Torch, light, fires of transformation, passion, illumination, regeneration, enlightenment, kinship.

Gebo "gay-bow" Gift, exchange of powers, relationships, exchanges, crossing paths or uniting, connections, balance.

Wunjo "woon-yo" Joy, perfection, shared goals, harmony of like forces, the best traits of all involved combined as a force, happiness.

Hagalaz "haw-gaw-laws" Hail, hailstone, disruption, destruction, seed form, moving ice, enduring and overcoming hardships.

Naudhiz "now-these" Need, necessity, distress, necessity is the mother of invention, resistance, friction creates fire.

Isa "ee-saw" Ice, contraction, stillness, suspension, introspection, restraint, slowed growth (can be beneficial), stagnation.

Jera "yare-awe" Harvest, year, season, cycles, the flow of life-death-rebirth, fruition, completion, reaping what you sow.

Continued next week. . .

Monday 6

Eta Aquarids

Islamic: Ramadan
Hidrellez (Hederlezi)

Tuesday 7

Eta Aquarids

Wednesday 8

Moon enters Cancer 4:07am

Thursday 9

Moon Opposition Saturn

Friday 10

Moon in Leo 8:14am
Christopher Penczak's Birthday

Saturday 11

◑ 8:13pm

Sunday 12

Moon in Virgo 11:22am
Mother's Day
Twi: 5:46am-Rise: 6:14am
Set: 8:07pm-Twi: 8:34pm

Rain washes away the negativity.

Runes

. . .Continued from last week.

Runes can be used to inscribe tools, or as sigil in spells. It is best to develop a good understanding of the runes before such use, and utilizing them as a divination tool will help you gain much insight.

Eihwaz "eye-wawz" Yew tree, axis of worlds, endings & beginnings, new opportunities, passages, between the worlds, protection.

Perthro "pear-throw" Dice cup, vulva, birth, problem solving, evolutionary force, "you buy your ticket-you take your ride".

Elhaz "ale-hawz" or "all-geese" Elk, protection, defense, support, luck, shielding, sanctuary, our connection with deity.

Sowilo "soe-wee-low" Sun, will, strength, victory, success, vitality, healing, solar energy and movement, directing power, clarity.

Tiwaz "tea-wawz" Creator, justice, success, responsibility, will, guided to success-truth-victory-justice-a good path, law & order.

Berkano "bear-kawn-oh" Birch tree, birch twig, life-death-rebirth, regeneration, growth, intuition, female fertility, new beginnings.

Ehwaz "ay-wawz" or "ay-woh" Horse, movement, connections, connecting with another force to move toward a goal.

Mannaz "mawn-nawz" Man (human), exams, disputes, challenges, arguments, gaining the upper hand, communication.

Laguz "law-gooze" Water, lake, flowing, emotions, intuition, psychic powers, revealing what is hidden (like beneath the water).

Ingwaz "eeeng-wawz" Fertility, Frey, potential energy, opportunity, how one thing ends affects how the next begins.

Dagaz "thaw-gauze" Day, a new day, new beginning, satisfactory or successful conclusion, positive end, final release.

Othala "oath-awe-law" Home, sacred ancestral land, inherited land, inheritance, ancestral power, true wealth and treasures.

Monday 13	Tuesday 14
4:52 pm	Alicia Bay Laurel's Birthday Moon in Libra 1:51pm
Wednesday 15	**Thursday 16** Beltania begins! ⟶ Moon in Scorpio 4:26pm
Friday 17	**Saturday 18** Moon in Sagittarius 8:21pm ◯ 4:12pm Omar Khayyam's Birthday
Sunday 19 ⟶ Last day of Beltania Malcolm X's Birthday Twi: 5:41am-Rise: 6:09am Set: 8:12pm-Twi: 8:40pm	Beltania is a MusicFest and Beltane Festival in Colorado, U.S.A.

You already have that which you seek.

The Wheel of the Year

The eight Sabbats marked in your almanac are the most widespread and popular. However, any given Sabbat may have multiple names and not every tradition celebrates the same Sabbats.

You will find that celebrating Sabbats will energize you, particularly if you are able to perform any type of ritual outdoors. Eventually, you will come to the point that you can feel a Sabbat drawing near.

Samhain is the beginning of the Wheel of the Year and is considered the "New Year" for many Witches. For some, this is the third and final harvest, and for many, it is a time to honor and celebrate ancestors. This Sabbat is called a "cross-quarter" because it falls about midway between an Equinox and a Solstice. The "veil between the worlds" is thought to be thin and Witches use divination or call upon the spirits of those who have crossed over.

Yule is also considered the New Year by some Witches and falls on the Winter Solstice. On Yule, we celebrate the rebirth of the Sun.

Imbolc brings an increase in warmth, the waxing of the light of the Sun and for many of us, the first stirrings of spring. As a cross-quarter, it falls about midway between the Solstice and Equinox.

Ostara is the Vernal or Spring Equinox. It is a time of rebirth within the Earth. Day and night are approximately equal.

Beltane is between the Equinox and the Solstice. As with Samhain, the "veil between the worlds" is thought to be thin at this time. This is the first day of summer and Earth is full of fertility and growth.

Midsummer is the Summer Solstice. This Sabbat is a celebration of the Sun at its peak and the warmth of the Earth. A very energetic time and traditionally a time for all types of spells and magic.

Lammas is a time of harvest as the bounty of the earth is reaching maturity. For some, it is the first of three harvest Sabbats.

Mabon is the Autumn Equinox and the second harvest for some. Celebrations of the harvest dominate this Sabbat.

Monday 20

Tuesday 21

Moon in Capricorn 2:57am
Sun enters Gemini 3:00am
Gwyddion Pendderwen's Birthday
Victor Anderson's Birthday

Wednesday 22

Thursday 23

Heartland Pagan Festival Begins
Moon in Aquarius 12:50pm

Friday 24

Saturday 25

Sunday 26

8:27 am

Moon in Pisces 1:08am
◐ 11:35am
Twi: 5:36am-Rise: 6:05am
Set: 8:17pm-Twi: 8:46pm

The Heartland Pagan Festival
is a large gathering held near
McLouth, Kansas, U.S.A.

Growth and comfort increase at home.

Candle Magic & Color Magic

Color magic is often practiced alongside candle magic. A candle color is chosen to assist the Witch in focusing on the True Goal. However, there are a variety of items you might choose to color coordinate with your magical work. If you are working on enhancing your psychic skills, you might choose a purple or violet cloth for wrapping your tarot cards. You could also try holding a purple amethyst or using a violet LED during meditation.

Learning color magic will help in other fields of study. Stone magic follows some of the associations of color magic, and learning Chakras is easier when you are familiar with the colors. E.g. Blue stones such as Lapis Lazuli, Sapphire and Celestite are used for psychic development and the third eye. Each element is associated with a color, and these correspondences vary among Witches.

The following are the most common associations. Feel free to note your own associations alongside them, and use your intuition.

Red: Lust, Passionate Love, Sexuality, Vigor, Magnetic, Virility

Pink: Unconditional Love, Self Love, Beauty, Emotional (rather than physical) Love, Friendship

Orange: Courage, Potency, Invigoration, Stimulation, Stamina

Yellow: Intellectual Stimulation, Warmth, General Attraction

Green: Fertility, Jealousy & Envy, Growth, Luck

Light Blue: Healing, Soothing, Peace, Spirituality, Devotion

Dark Blue & Indigo: Psychic Enhancement, Intuition, Wisdom

Violet: Connection to the Divine, Spirituality, Air of Distinction, Expansion, Magic, Influencing Others

Black: Absorbs, Banishing, Reversing Spells, Negativity, Grounding, Protection

White: Protection, General Use, Peace, Purity, Tranquility

Silver: The Moon, Feminine Principle, Clairvoyance, Goddess

Gold: The Sun, Masculine Principle, Wealth, God

Monday 27
Heartland Pagan Festival ends.

Morning Glory
Zell-Ravenheart's Birthday

Federal: Memorial Day

Tuesday 28

Moon in Aries 1:32pm

Wednesday 29

Thursday 30

Moon in Taurus 11:43pm
Joan of Arc Day

Friday 31

Saturday 1

Mormon: Brigham Young's Birthday

Sunday 2

Moon in Gemini 6:48am
Anniversary of Citizenship Granted
to Native American Indians
Twi: 5:33am-Rise: 6:02am
Set: 8:22pm-Twi: 8:51pm

LGBT: June is Pride Month!
This year's theme:
"Millions of Moments of Pride"
Host City: Athens, Greece

Amazing activities in New York
City all month celebrating
Worldpride | Stonewall 50

Your horizons expand this week.

Herbs to Empower Your Food

We all know about adding some basil to our pasta or ginger to pumpkin pie, but there are many herbs in a Witch's cupboard that can be used in everyday cooking to add nutrition and magic.

Chamomile is anti-inflammatory and lends an apple-honey fragrance to baked goods. Chamomile's association with the sun makes it an excellent choice for solar Sabbat feasts. Grind the contents of chamomile tea bags in a pestle and mortar, blender, or coffee grinder and add the powder to cookies or cakes. You can add a tablespoon of the ground flowers to most recipes that make a dozen servings without other adjustments.

Cinnamon has been linked to regulating blood sugar levels and is magically used for prosperity and attraction. Almost any chocolate recipe can be enhanced with just a whisper of cinnamon. Add a pinch to your next batch of brownies to see how cinnamon does not have to taste like pumpkin pie, it can enhance and deepen chocolate notes.

Lavender is relaxing and provides protection and clarity of thought. A pinch of the flowers adds dimension to savory soups and is a great pick-me-up when someone is under the weather.

Calendula flower petals are rich in anti-oxidants and add a bright, sunny splash to salads. They are said to renew personal power and assist in clear thinking and legal matters.

Violet flowers are another great salad sprinkle, especially for romantic meals. Used for attraction, love, and lust, they are also wonderful when candied.

Rose petals gathered from organic sources can also be candied or added to salads. They are rich in anti-oxidants and are used for love, divination, and friendship.

Juniper Berries are said to protect against harm, especially theft or accidents, and are used for attraction. A few berries can be added to roasted vegetables or meats for a delightful flavor boost.

Monday 3

Marion Zimmer
Bradley's Birthday   ● 5:03am

Tuesday 4

Moon enters Cancer 4:17pm

Wednesday 5

Thursday 6

Moon Opposition Saturn
Moon enters Leo 7:16pm

Friday 7

British Museum
Founded 1753   6:15pm

Saturday 8

World Oceans Day
Moon enters Virgo 9:45pm

Sunday 9

Puerto Rican Day Parades
Twi: 5:31am-Rise: 6:01am
Set: 8:26pm-Twi: 8:55pm

Good memories and faces appear from your past.

What's the Deal With 93?

While rubbing shoulders with other Witches or occultists, you may come across the number 93. You may even see it used as a greeting like a secret handshake. But what does it mean?

93 is the numerical value of Thelema (the Greek word for Will). It is also the numerical equivalent for the Greek word *agape*, meaning love. People who follow Thelemic paths base much of their information on the works of Aleister Crowley as he developed the religion. **Thelema** or Will is expressed as: *Do what thou wilt shall be the whole of the Law.* **Agape** or Love is expressed as: *Love is the law, love under will.*

These two phrases are the Law of Thelema. In the Thelemic Order of the Golden Dawn (T∴G∴D∴) and a few other magickal orders, members honor each other by saying the Thelema part and the person being greeted then says the agape part in response.

These phrases can be used as both greetings and farewells; the greeting being Thelema, and the parting being agape.

The abbreviation (93) developed as a shortcut and code in written correspondence, and the number represents the entire Law of Thelema. You may see 93 in the signature line of an email or 93/93 in a text message. Numerologically, the sum of the values of the letters in the word Thelema total 93. Also, the sum of the values of the letters in the word agape total 93.

Only a small fraction of Witches are also Thelemites, but when you meet one and come across 93, now you'll know what it means.

Monday 10

◗ 1:00am

Jupiter bright in the sky, view
four moons with binoculars.

Tuesday 11

Free Spirit Gathering Begins
Moon enters Libra 12:29am

Wednesday 12

Anne Frank's Birthday

Thursday 13

Gerald Gardner's Birthday
Moon enters Scorpio 4:03

Friday 14

Saturday 15

Moon enters Sagittarius 9:03am

Sunday 16

Valentina Tereshkova:
first woman in space 1963

Free Spirit Gathering Ends

Pagan Spirit
Gatherin begins   Father's Day

Twi: 5:31am-Rise: 6:00am
Set: 8:29pm-Twi: 8:58pm

The Free Spirit Gathering is
a large conference and celebration
held in Darlington, MD

The Pagan Spirit Gathering is
one of the largest and oldest
gatherings of Pagan paths in
the U.S. held near Oxford, OH

Communication strains are temporary; keep your perspective.

The 13 Principles of Witchcraft

In April of 1974, a group of around seventy-three Pagans and Witches of varying traditions came together in Minneapolis, Minnesota. This *Council of American Witches* disbanded later the same year. However, while they were convened they attempted to form a statement of common principles and definitions shared by Witches in order to dispel misinformation. These principles have been incorporated into one or more editions of the U.S. Army handbook for chaplains.

Not every Witch will agree with each of these principles, but many agree on at least a few. Comments and notations in italics are from the authors of your almanac and were not part of the original text. These notes are included for your study, or just as trivia.

Introduction:

"In seeking to be inclusive, we do not wish to open ourselves to the destruction of our group by those on self-serving power trips, or to philosophies and practices contradictory to those principles. In seeking to exclude those whose ways are contradictory to ours, we do not want to deny participation with us to any who are sincerely interested in our knowledge and beliefs, regardless of race, color, sex, age, national or cultural origins or sexual preference."

Principles of Belief:

1. We practice rites to attune ourselves with the natural rhythm of life forces marked by the phases of the Moon and the seasonal Quarters and Cross Quarters. *Usually in the form of Sabbat and Esbat celebrations.*

2. We recognize that our intelligence gives us a unique responsibility toward our environment. We seek to live in harmony with Nature, in ecological balance offering fulfillment to life and consciousness within an evolutionary concept.

Continued next week. . .

Monday 17

Starhawk's Birthday ◯ 3:32am
Moon enters Capricorn 4:15pm

Tuesday 18

Sally Ride: First U.S.
woman in space 1983

Wednesday 19

Juneteenth

Thursday 20

Moon enters Aquarius 2:01am

Solstice Friday 21

10:54am

Moon enters Pisces 2:02pm
Sun enters Cancer 10:55am

Saturday 22

Sunday 23

Look west just after sunset to see
Mercury on the horizon

Pagan Spirit
Gathering ends   2:49am

Twi: 5:32am-Rise: 6:02am
Set: 8:30pm-Twi: 9:00pm

Powerful energies are in the air this week; breathe deeply!

3. We acknowledge a depth of power far greater than that apparent to the average person. Because it is far greater than ordinary it is sometimes called "supernatural", but we see it as lying within that which is naturally potential to all.

4. We conceive of the Creative Power in the universe as manifesting through polarity-as masculine and feminine-and that this same Creative Power lies in all people, and functions through the interaction of the masculine and feminine. We value neither (gender) above the other, knowing each to be supportive to the other. *This next section of #4 is often omitted in recent copies, partly because of residual puritanical beliefs in the public and in. . .*

From "How to Write a Love Letter" on Page 2 of Safe Counsel:
Searchlights on Health: Light on Dark Corners (1896)

Monday 24	Tuesday 25
	◑ 4:47am
Janet Farrar's Birthday	Moon enters Aries 2:38am

Wednesday 26	Thursday 27
Stonewall Rebellions 1969	Scott Cunningham's Birthday
WorldPride Opening Ceremony	Moon enters Taurus 1:32pm
begins in New York City	Helen Keller's Birthday

Friday 28	Saturday 29
Stewart Farrar's Birthday	Moon enters Gemini 9:09pm

Sunday 30	
WorldPride Closing Ceremony	
and PrideFest in New York City	
Twi: 5:34am-Rise: 6:04am	
Set: 8:31pm-Twi: 9:01pm	Work towards loving others.

Judicious choices by yourself and others are in your favor.

some modern Witches, and partly because it is often misunderstood: We value sex as pleasure, as the symbol and embodiment of life, and as one of the sources of energies used in magickal practice and religious worship.

5. We recognize both outer worlds and inner, or psychological, worlds sometimes known as the Spiritual World, the Collective Unconscious, Inner Planes, etc.-and we see in the interaction of these two dimensions the basis for paranormal phenomena and magickal exercises. We neglect neither dimension for the other, seeing both as necessary for our fulfillment.

6. We do not recognize any authoritarian hierarchy but do honor those who teach, respect those who share their greater knowledge and wisdom, and acknowledge those who have courageously given of themselves in leadership.

7. We see religion, magick, and wisdom in living as being united in the way one views the world and lives within it-a worldview and philosophy of life which we identify as Witchcraft-the Wiccan Way.

8. Calling oneself "Witch" does not make a Witch-but neither. . .

In Needwood Forest
from The Story of Some English Shires by Mandell Creighton, 1897

Monday 1

Moon enters Cancer 8:24pm

Tuesday 2

2:23pm:
Total, not visible

● 2:17pm
Thurgood Marshall's Birthday

Wednesday 3

Moon Opposition Saturn
Moon enters Leo 10:20pm

Thursday 4

Independence Day
Aphelion: Earth is farthest
from the sun in its orbit

Friday 5

12:00am   Moon enters
         Virgo 11:26pm

Saturday 6

Frida Kahlo's Birthday
Tibetan: 14th Dalai Lama's
Birthday (won Nobel Peace Prize)

Sunday 7

Retro ♀ ♂
6:14pm

Twi: 5:38am-Rise: 6:07am
Set: 8:30pm-Twi: 9:00pm

Family and home are happier, and more stable.

does heredity itself, nor the collecting of titles, degrees, and initiations. A Witch seeks to control the forces within her/himself that make life possible in order to live wisely and will without harm to other and in harmony with Nature.

9. We believe in the affirmation and fulfillment of life in a continuation of evolution and development of consciousness giving meaning to the Universe we know and our personal role within it.

10. Our only animosity towards Christianity, or toward any other religion or philosophy of life, is to the extent that its institutions have claimed to be "the only way" and have sought to deny freedom to others and to suppress other ways of religious practice and belief.

11. As American Witches, we are not threatened by debates on the history of the Craft, the origins of various terms, the legitimacy of various aspects of different traditions. We are concerned with our present and our future.

12. We do not accept the concept of absolute evil, nor do we worship any entity known as "Satan" or "the Devil", as defined by Christian tradition. We do not seek power through the suffering of others, nor accept that personal benefit can be derived only by denial to another.

13. We believe that we should seek within Nature that which is contributory to our health and well-being.

Witches' Symbols of Protection

Witch's Knot   Pentacle   Triquetra

Monday 8

Moon enters Libra 1:07am

Tuesday 9

Starwood Festival begins

◑ 5:56am
Saturn energy is strong and the planet is visible all night

Wednesday 10

Moon enters Scorpio 4:29am

Thursday 11

Friday 12

Moon enters Sagittarius 10:05am

Saturday 13

Witchfest begins
Margaret Murray's Birthday

Sunday 14

Moon enters
Capricorn 6:05pm

Witchfest ends
Bastille Day
Twi: 5:42am-Rise: 6:11am
Set: 8:28pm-Twi: 8:57pm

The Starwood Festival is a large Neo-Pagan, New Age, multi-cultural and world music festival held at Wisteria in Ohio, U.S.A.

Witchfest is a large Pagan street faire in Manhattan, New York

Sometimes destruction brings just the change that is needed.

What do Modern Witches Believe?

Not all Witches agree with the 13 Principles, so what do they agree upon? Witches have ideas, concepts, and theories more than they have beliefs. The Craft is ever-changing and does not have dogma or doctrine. Every Witch has a slightly different idea/belief, and that idea might change frequently. It is this flexibility that always keeps the Craft modern.

This does not mean that Witches are without a strong set of ethics and a sense of personal responsibility. You will find that seasoned Witches are generally some of the most thoughtful and conscientious people you encounter.

Because of this diverse tapestry of ideas, only those ideas held by the majority of Witches are noted here. It is up to you to determine if any of these ideas resonate with you.

Overall: Nearly all Witches feel that it is important to look within for answers. Connecting with nature and deity on a personal level, experimentation, and independent thought are all encouraged.

Harmony: Witches generally believe that living in harmony with the earth, nature, people, the cycles of nature, the planets, and the universe as a whole, is an integral part of their spiritual path.

Honoring & Celebrating Natural Cycles: Most Witches honor the changing of the seasons and the cycles of nature on Sabbats. Many Witches also honor the energy of the Moon on Esbats, celebrations held on the full or sometimes new moon.

Magic & Spells: We acknowledge that there are forces in the universe that science has not yet identified and that these forces can be influenced to bend reality toward our goals.

What Goes Around Comes Around: Most Witches follow the Rede or similar code that reminds us to <u>own</u> our magic and actions. The basic tenets expressed in the Rede, *Do as ye will, an it harm none*, are expressed in many different cultures and philosophies around the world, but all have a common thread of truth.

Monday 15

Starwood Festival Ends

☽ Tuesday 16

4:31pm
Partial,
not visible

◯ 4:39pm

Wednesday 17

Moon enters Aquarius 4:19am

Thursday 18

Nelson Mandela's Birthday

Friday 19

San Francisco Public Library
starts lending books 1880
Moon enters Pisces 4:19pm

Saturday 20

6:58 pm   Apollo II Moon
Walk 1969

Sunday 21

Twi: 5:47am-Rise: 6:16am
Set: 8:25pm-Twi: 8:54pm

Focus on your craft and skills, the rest will follow.

Visualization Exercises

Visualization is an important tool for achieving your goals. It may be frustrating at first, but eventually, you will be able to bring images to your mind in great detail. Our lives are filled with visual stimuli. Stories are watched on screens that fill in all the visuals for us. To increase your visualization skills, listen to audiobooks, read descriptive stories, and daydream! To speed your progress, try the following exercises. Eyes can be open or closed, and sit or lie in any comfortable position. Struggling? Skip to another exercise, but be sure to come back to the ones that tripped you up.

Color Fields: Visualize a solid color field starting with red. Try to see only that color. Move on through the rainbow (Chakra colors) to orange, then yellow, green, blue, indigo, and violet.

Color Shapes: Imagine a red circle, switch to orange, yellow, green, blue, indigo, violet.

3D Color Shapes: Picture a red sphere or ball. Switch to orange, yellow, green, etc. as in other exercises.

Moving Color Shapes: Picture a field of red. Now imagine that a letter, such as your first initial, is rising out of the color field as if it were surfacing from a pool of water. Once it has surfaced, try to spin the letter around in your mind as if it were a rotating sign. Continue through the rainbow colors and try different letters and numbers.

Complex Shapes: Place a nick-nack, coffee mug, alarm clock or another object in front of you. Look at it carefully, then look away or close your eyes and try to bring the image of the object into your mind as clearly as possible.

Tactile Visualization: Visualize a sphere of color as you did in the 3D Color Shape exercise. Now make the sphere glow with energy and move it into a palm of your hand. Continue to develop your visualization until you can feel the sphere. It may feel like a tickle, a pulsating beat, or even a warm or cold sensation.

Monday 22

Moon enters Aries 5:03am
Sun enters Leo 9:51pm

Tuesday 23

Wednesday 24

Marvin the Martian first
on Looney Tunes 1948
Moon enters
Taurus 4:43pm   ◑ 8:19pm

Thursday 25

Friday 26

Americans with Disabilities Act
goes into effect July 26, 1990

Saturday 27

Moon enters Gemini 1:29am

Sunday 28
Delta Aquariids

Twi: 5:53am-Rise: 6:21am
Set: 8:20pm-Twi: 8:48pm

Your words can be used as a gift or a weapon.

Stone Magic

Stones are excellent tools for spells and magic. You can use them in pouches, carry them as an amulet, incorporate them into tools, and use them as wards. This correspondence list will help you select the stone that fits your needs. These stone profiles reflect our experiences, so please remember that you may feel a different energy from a type of stone and that every stone has its own 'personality'.

Amazonite: A type of feldspar used for harmony, blending many energies, peace, calm, communication.

Amber: A powerful amulet and traditional Witch's 'stone' for good reason. The most ancient stone used for amulets and magic. Solar and light energy. Very energizing, increases power, purification and protection from negativity, psychic and magical vampirism; shielding (without hiding).

Amethyst: Enhances general magical workings and raises personal power. To fine-tune its energy, combine amethyst with other stones and focus clearly on your goals and intent. Well suited to psychic development, protection, detoxification, inner exploration, emotional and psychic shielding, purification, breaking addictions, self-understanding.

Apache Tears: A special variety of volcanic obsidian used for protection and shielding, emotional cleansing, grounding. Brings protective earth energy to sensitive psychics and empaths.

Black Tourmaline: Protection and purification. Probably the best all-around protection stone. Tends to need less cleansing than many stones. Shielding, grounding, neutralizing, detoxification, prevents psychic and magical drain, anti-hex, converts negative energy into neutral energy.

Bloodstone: A red and green chalcedony used for strength, healing, courage, detoxification, purification. Very balancing, energizing and grounding of sexual and emotional centers for. . .

Monday 29

Delta Aquariids

Moon enters Cancer 6:31am

Tuesday 30

Moon Opposition Saturn

Wednesday 31

Direct ☿
10:58pm

Moon enters
Leo 8:18am   ● 10:13pm

Thursday 1

Friday 2

2:11 am
Moon enters Virgo 8:21am

Saturday 3

Sunday 4

Moon enters Libra 8:30am
Twi: 5:58am-Rise: 6:26am
Set: 8:15pm-Twi: 8:42pm

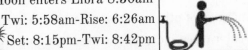

Appreciate the present with your family and friends.

healing the body and spirit. Combines well with other stones and spell ingredients. (Works and plays well with others.)

Botswana Agate: Soothing and energizing, like a spa treatment for the spirit. For manifesting higher goals, clearing conflict, harmonizing, absorbs negative energy (cleanse stone well) and prevents unwanted visitors (physical, psychic, dimensional, etc.). Cuts ties to the past, psychic links, hexes, addictions & negative patterns. Helps prevent dwelling/obsessing on the negative; helps find solutions.

Carnelian: Orange-red and usually semi-translucent. For focus, concentration, uplifting, energizing, protection. Prevents psychic and emotional drain. Helps reinforce aura, increase confidence, improve motivation. Brings an energizing life force for creativity, personal will, and sexuality.

Celestite: Also known as Celestine, this rare mineral is used to help you connect with your higher self, tune-in to your deeper goals, face your shadows, and for dream work. Very healing when working through issues in order to reclaim your personal power, and open your flow of energy to that of the universe. With time, this use also helps with manifestation of your true goals and desires in the physical plane.

Citrine: A quartz in the yellow hues, from lemon-yellow to root beer amber. Very energizing and enlightening. Used for manifestation of creativity. Brightens mood, boosts your 'inner fire' and protects against negativity.

Clear Quartz: Power, protection, harmony, energy. These power-houses will boost the energy of any healing, energy work, ritual tool or talisman. Whether tumbled smooth or in their original pointed crystal form, they add their energy to the overall working according to your will and focus, while providing clarity and helping harmonize mixed energies of other stones, other people's wills, etc.

Fluorite: The color often indicates its uses, ranging from green (healing) to purple (psychic work) and more. Very high energy in. . .

Monday 5

Tuesday 6

Moon enters Scorpio 3:32pm

Wednesday 7

Thursday 8

2:19pm   ◖12:32pm Moon enters Sagittarius 3:35pm

Friday 9

Saturday 10

Look for Mercury low in the
East just before Sunrise   Moon enters Capricorn 11:50pm

Sunday 11

Twi: 6:04am-Rise: 6:31am
Set: 8:08pm-Twi: 8:35pm

Take a little "me time" to relax and love yourself.

the mind and crown chakra. It can help to open doors of perception, improve mental clarity for decision making, divination or study. Very cleansing and purifying, will remove negativity and is a great 'junk eraser' after healing, psychic, ritual, spell and magical work.

Garnet: Healing broken hearts, physical health, strength, sexual expression, self-worth, attraction, lust, sexual love, protection. Used to invoke the symbolism of the pomegranate. Earth energy, fertility.

Goldstone: Helps you focus on and achieve your goals; increases ambition and drive; emotionally stabilizing; protection; uplifting. Has a slight tendency to attract money.

Green Aventurine: A green quartz stone with mica inclusions. Increases opportunities, confidence, growth, personal energy, vitality, and perception. Aventurine is often used for luck; helping you take advantage of opportunities, and allowing you to better perceive opportunities as they arise. Traditionally used to attract adventure and for general attraction, creating a positive attitude, fortifying independence; said by some practitioners to invoke the favor of the Goddess of Love.

Hawk's Eye: A 'tiger's eye' stone in the colors of blue, green and gray. For clarity and gaining perspective, psychic work and visions, opening the third eye, protection while doing visualization, divination, and magic. Eye stones are often used for luck, helping you take advantage of opportunities, or helping you to perceive opportunities as they arise. Psychic, mental and emotional stamina.

Hematite: An iron oxide mineral. Manifestation, potency, charisma, grounding, balancing of opposites, detoxification, strength, and courage; can be used in spells for removing insecurity or even impotence.

Jet: A very powerful amulet used since ancient times for protection, purification, manifestation on the physical plane, stress relief, dispelling negative patterns within and without, grounding (without heaviness). Prevents psychic and magical vampirism, . . .

Monday 12
Perseids

Tuesday 13
Perseids

Moon enters Aquarius 10:36am

Wednesday 14

Thursday 15

Moon enters Pisces 10:50pm

◯ 7:30am

Charles Godfrey Leland's Birthday

Friday 16

Saturday 17

5:49 am

Sunday 18

Moon enters Aries 11:33am
Twi: 6:10am-Rise: 6:36am
Set: 8:00pm-Twi: 8:26pm

Carrot: Items found or returned. Stick: Leave behind old habits and patterns.

purification, helps channel earth energies. Lunar and shadow energy. A traditional Witch's 'stone' with good reason.

Kyanite: Mental and psychic clarity; stays clear for better purification and protection; quick access to visualization, magickal powers, telepathy, and intuition. Unlocks the third eye, helps you understand how to use your skills responsibly. Aids in communication, expression, balance, dream work, meditation.

Lapis Lazuli: Creativity, visualization, expression, articulation, communication, intuition, useful for divination and psychic readings. Helps you tap into your psychic centers to aid in gathering and directing your energy, raising power for magick and spells, visualizing and manifesting goals.

Mahogany Obsidian: Promotes inner strength & healing; reduces feelings of unworthiness; amazing ability to end psychic attacks & psychic "chains" or "ties" placed either consciously or subconsciously by others. Stabilizing & grounding for better manifestation & healing. Unblocking, protection, gently grounding.

Malachite: Useful for analyzing repeated negative patterns, draws out repressed memories and emotions, good for revealing and healing emotional damage and trauma. Helps heal broken hearts.

Mook Jasper: A micro-crystalline quartz. Helps tune into earth energies, cycles, and patterns. Excellent for maintaining the sense of wonder and openness of youth, thereby increasing opportunities and a sense of gratitude.

Moonstone: Self-acceptance, self-confidence, tuning into your intuition and psychic centers, soothing, balancing and calming, dream work, shadow work, working with cycles and patterns, feminine power, intuition, Goddess energy, inspiration, creativity.

Picture Jasper: Banded with many colors, the patterns in the stone sometimes resemble a landscape. Tuning into earth energies, harmonizing multiple energies, gaining perspective and insight for physical manifestations (redecorating, garden plans, business plans). Visualization, nurturing, confidence. . .

Monday 19	Tuesday 20
	Moon enters Taurus 11:37pm
Wednesday 21	**Thursday 22**
Friday 23	**Saturday 24**
◗ 9:57am Moon enters Gemini 9:34am Sun enters Virgo 5:02am	
Sunday 25	
Moon enters Cancer 4:06pm Twi: 6:15am-Rise: 6:41am Set: 7:51pm-Twi: 8:17pm	

The world is at your fingertips this week, and a woman offers good counsel.

Red Jasper: A micro-crystalline quartz. A very useful stone you will reach for again and again. Balancing, handling emotional stress, retaining dreams and visions, enhancing physical strength and inner stability. Gently grounding. Has a good healing energy, especially in the lower chakra centers.

Red Tiger's Eye & Golden Cat's Eye: Found in red (tiger), gold and yellow (cat) and used for protection, perception, clear thinking, discovering the truth, and increasing luck. Like Aventurine, eye stones are often used for general luck, but this is primarily due to their ability to help you take advantage of opportunities by increasing your ability to perceive both opportunities and pitfalls as they arise. Excellent for enhancing and focusing willpower, protection, grounding, vitality, motivation, balance, insight and integrity. Also used for psychic, mental and emotional stamina; and for seeing your way clearly.

Rhodonite: Pink and black coloration is a reminder of the grounding and centering of this stone's energy. It helps to stabilize emotions and ground the heart chakra for better healing. A stone of grace, discovering hidden talents, generosity, and compassion, expression of love, understanding your purpose.

Rose Quartz: Pink shades of micro-crystalline quartz, usually found in mass rather than individual crystals. Heals emotions, self-love & self-acceptance. Dissipates negativity, anger, tension & frustration. For unconditional love, self-acceptance, beauty, allowing love in, creativity; enhances receptivity to love; prevents fighting and encourages harmony, friendship, and peace.

Ruby: Increases life force, courage, confidence; invokes sensuality and passion; attracts people towards the wearer. Energizes and activates all energy centers; Boosts motivation; helps aspire to new levels.

Sapphire: Balancing, healing & soothing; Increases awareness and personal power. Said to ensure faithfulness and protect relationships from love triangles. . .

Monday 26	Tuesday 27
Moon Opposition Saturn Women's Equality Day	Moon enters Leo 6:54pm

Wednesday 28	Thursday 29
	Moon enters Virgo 6:58pm

Friday 30	Saturday 31
10:53am 5:38am	Moon enters Libra 6:08pm Raymond Buckland's Birthday Islamic: Al-Hijra (New Year) 1441

Sunday 1
Twi: 6:21am-Rise: 6:47am Set: 7:42pm-Twi: 8:08pm

Money lags a tad, but emotions are in balance.

Selenite: A soft stone with a powerful punch. Helps to direct energy to your will and goals, aids in communicating with other realms, clears the cobwebs from the third eye and crown to enhance perception. Increase awareness, psychic skills & insight. Harmoniously blends & amplifies other stones.

Shiva Lingham: Meditation, insight, healing, very balancing & energizing, psychic skills, high spiritual vibrations, union of opposites, manifestation of wisdom. Healing of emotional and sexual issues, reclaiming sexual power and increasing self-love. Understanding and trusting the positive masculine.

Smokey Quartz: Protective of sensitive people, helping to guard against over-empathizing, being suckered by con artists, and helps prevent unhealthy relationships with others. Both grounding and uplifting, it is often used to move energy through all the seven major chakras. Pairs well with amethyst.

Snowflake Obsidian: You will love this stone so much that even after decades of use, you will find yourself coming back to it. While grounding, centering and protecting, it brings hidden things to the surface. You can use this energy for emotional and physical healing, psychic awareness and even for spells to return lost objects. Helps one to see patterns for better psychic readings and mental health.

Sodalite: A fantastic writer's stone for inspiration and any creative pursuit involving intelligence, communication, education (teaching and learning), creativity, foresight, and logic.

Spirit Quartz: Found in amethyst, clear and other types of quartz, these special formations are a larger crystal covered in many smaller druzy quartz crystals. Gaining perspective, increasing humor and ability to experience joy, reducing fears and anxiety, moving on, speeds and enhances magical workings, great for covens as it helps many people work toward a common goal, heals discord, increases patience, will receive a magical charge well, making it well suited to talismans and wards. Projects a charge well.

Staurolite Crystal: Also called fairy cross. Symbolizes the. . .

Monday 2

Federal: Labor Day
Hindu: Ganesh Chaturthi
in honor of the god Ganesha
Moon enters Scorpio 6:35pm

Tuesday 3

Wednesday 4

Moon enters Sagittarius 10:08pm

Thursday 5

◑ 10:12pm
Tashunka Witko
Crazy Horse's Birthday

Friday 6

Saturday 7

Moon enters Capricorn 5:38am

Sunday 8

Twi: 6:26am-Rise: 6:52am
Set: 7:32pm-Twi: 7:58pm

Good financial week. Relationships: focus on what you already or still have.

crossing of paths on the universal web, invokes the favor of the Fates or Goddess of Crossroads. Helps protect against hexes, negativity & rebound from magical work and spells.

Tiger Iron: A very powerful combination of red jasper, tiger eye, and hematite. Harmoniously blends all of the energies of these three stones. Great for manifestation, protection, energy, strength, stamina, increases willpower, motivation, bringing insights into action, healing, and grounding, creative solutions.

Tourmalated Quartz: A powerful shield of protection and neutralization of negative energy. Stays clear a long time, making it perfect as a 'take with you' charm. Energizing and grounding at the same time. Good for purification.

Unakite: A green and pink jasper (micro-crystalline quartz) that balances and heals the heart, helps manifest love, calms, stabilizing, prevents ego-based negative patterns, releasing.

Watermelon Tourmaline: Balances the heart, encourages self-love while healing and recovering from negative relationship or past mistakes. Increases your magnetism and attraction for your positive benefit. Tends to protect you from spells cast by others, but this energy is more prominent in black tourmaline.

Wavellite: A powerful mineral found in Arkansas near the place where some of the best magical quartz crystals come from. Extremely useful for tuning into earth energies, manifestation, understanding interconnectedness, healing emotions, finding your path and making decisions. Excellent for healing, increasing your sense of well-being, changing your perspective when you are feeling down or 'stuck' and helps you gain insight.

Zebra Stone: Helps you see yourself and others clearly. Grounds high energy without being too heavy, it helps to manifest goals on the material plane. Unconditional love, helps harmonize varied energies of numerous stones or ingredients in a spell or talisman. Combats depression, apathy, and disinterest; increases creativity and motivation; a nurturing & protective energy.

Monday 9

Moon enters Aquarius 4:24pm
Neptune is a tiny blue spot
in the sky all night long

Tuesday 10

Carl Llewellyn Weschcke's Birthday

Wednesday 11

Silver RavenWolf's Birthday

Thursday 12

Moon enters Pisces 4:52am

Friday 13

○ 11:34pm   8:32am

Saturday 14

Moon enters Aries 5:33pm

Sunday 15

National Hispanic Heritage Month
begins Sept. 15 and ends Oct. 15

Twi: 6:31am-Rise: 6:56am
Set: 7:22pm-Twi: 7:48pm

Your skills improve rapidly. Proficiency leads to profit.

Balms, Unguents, Salves & Ointments

Balms are the potions of healers, and making balms is fun, easy, and can save you money. A standard lip balm formula is about 3P Oil to 1P Wax. For this 3:1 ratio, melt 1 teaspoon of beeswax and slowly add 3 teaspoons of olive oil while continuing to heat on low. A double boiler or a heat-proof glass jar in a pan of water works best to prevent scorching. For a softer balm, add a bit more oil, about a ¼ part. The addition of essential oils (EO) will also change your oil-to-wax ratio and yield a slightly softer balm. In hot weather, you may wish to add just a bit more wax so your balm is not overly prone to melting.

A hard salve can be made with 4P Oil to 1P Wax. This is a good formula for delivering controlled amounts of medicinal oils.

Lip Balm 3:1
Hard Salve 4:1
Ointment 5:1

Oregano salve works as a decent antiseptic, but too much of the oil can be damaging. A few drops of Oregano EO in this 4:1 formula will create a good balm for twist-up applicators like lip balm tubes, deodorant tubes, or body butter holders. The oil ratio is high enough that the salve isn't too sticky, and will slide over scratches without dragging.

A softer ointment or unguent similar to lip balms sold in small jars can be achieved with the formula of 5P Oil to 1P wax. This formula melts at a temperature close to that of the skin. To firm it up slightly without going as far as a hard salve, use plant butters in place of some or all of the oil. Shea butter, mango butter, cocoa butter, and coconut oil will work to firm up any balm. This is a good formula for soft calendula and comfrey balms.

Try infusing your oils with herbs before you make them into balm. Consider other types of wax such as vegetable or carnauba.

Monday 16

Moon enters Taurus 5:31am

Tuesday 17

Wednesday 18

Cecil Hugh Williamson's Birthday

Thursday 19

Moon enters Gemini 3:58pm

Arrgh! International Talk Like a Pirate Day

Friday 20

Saturday 21

◑ 9:42pm
Moon enters Cancer 11:50pm
International Day of Peace

Sunday 22

Twi: 6:36am-Rise: 7:02am
Set: 7:12pm-Twi: 7:38pm

A high energy week filled with abundance.

Spell to Gain Psychic Abilities

There is a spark of psychic ability in every person. This spell, along with the visualization exercises in your almanac, taps into your natural abilities so you gain better understanding and control.

☐ **Cedar Incense**
Select a natural incense with real cedar.

☐ **Organic, Natural Earl Grey Tea**
You can use the Goddess Grey Recipe found in your almanac after this spell, or choose a high-quality brand that uses natural Bergamot essential oil, *Citrus bergamia*

☐ **1 Stone:** A small tumble-polished Lapis Lazuli or Sodalite, or a small Amethyst, Celestite, or Blue Kyanite crystal.

☐ **3 drops Frankincense EO**

☐ **5mL (1 teaspoon) Carrier Oil in a Small Vial**
You will be anointing your skin with this oil so choose a good carrier such as olive, almond, avocado, sunflower or jojoba.

☐ **1 Blue or Purple Candle**

At any time on the day or night of the Full Moon, add the Frankincense oil to your carrier oil while saying Words of Power (WoP) of your own creation, or: *My eyes are open as these words are spoken.* Next, brew a cup of tea and sit comfortably in a quiet place with your spell components assembled in front of you, don't forget a lighter or matches!

Light the incense while saying WoP or: *Breath and air bring insight to me.* Light the candle while saying your WoP or: *My mind alights with the visions I seek.*

Close your eyes and breathe deeply. Hold the cup of tea up to your mouth and breathe in the aroma. Sip as desired while you relax and empty your mind into the moment. . .

Monday 23

Equinox

2:51am

Sun enters
Libra 2:51am
Moon Opposition Saturn

Tuesday 24

Moon enters Leo 4:20am

Wednesday 25

Thursday 26

Equilux at 35° North*
Moon enters Virgo 5:37am

Friday 27

9:24pm

Saturday 28

● 1:27pm
Moon enters Libra 5:03am

Sunday 29

Jewish: Rosh Hashanah
Twi: 6:42am-Rise: 7:07am
Set: 7:03pm-Twi: 7:28pm

* Equilux is when day and
night appear equal based on
your Latitude. This is usually
a few days after the Equinox.

Your achievements bring great satisfaction, a good harvest.

Anoint your third eye (above/between your eyebrows) and inner wrists with a drop of the oil blend while saying your WoP or: *I am one with all that is around me, I open my eyes to be truly free.*

Hold the stone you have chosen in the palm of your hand and continue to clear your mind and relax. Once you feel completely at ease, you may begin some of the visualization exercises here in your almanac. Go through them casually, delving into one, then try another. Let go of any frustration and simply let your mind find its own footing so to speak.

When the incense has gone out, or after about a half hour to an hour, begin to come out of your spellwork. Allow your mind to become more aware of your surroundings, feel the seat under you and become more present in your physical body. With your eyes open, stand and say confirmation WoP or: *So mote it be!*

Carry the stone with you whenever you need to be more in tune with your psychic powers. Every time you repeat the spell, your stone will gain a stronger charge of energy.

This spell will increase your psychic awareness immediately. As the years go by, you will find that you no longer need this spell, but that it is very balancing for use before divination sessions such as scrying, tarot, or rune readings. It also gives you balance and openness when you are stressed and feel that your psychic abilities are scattered, or when you just can't seem to "connect".

Note that the four Classic Elements are used in this spell. It is a tidy bit of natural magic that has a strong foundation in both Witchcraft and psychology. You can modify this spell for other purposes, substituting WoP and ingredients. For success you might choose a green candle, patchouli incense, aventurine stone and an earthy/smokey tea such as Pu Erh or Lapsang Souchong, To add a prosperity and money boost, you might try champagne, apple cider, cyser or mead. Feel free to experiment and develop your own!

Monday 30

Moon enters Scorpio 4:42am

Tuesday 1

Isaac Bonewits's Birthday

Wednesday 2

Moon enters Sagittarius 6:45am
Mahatma Gandhi's Birthday

Thursday 3

Friday 4

Moon enters Capricorn 12:44pm

Saturday 5

☽ 11:48am

Sunday 6

Moon enters Aquarius 10:43pm
Fannie Lou Hamer's Birthday
German American Heritage Day

Twi: 6:47am-Rise: 7:12am
Set: 6:53pm-Twi: 7:18pm

October is:
Breast Cancer Awareness Month
Global Diversity Awareness Month

This week you reap abundance and prosperity from your hard work.

Goddess Grey - Tea Recipe

2.5 mL (½ teaspoon) Bergamot Essential Oil - try organic, FCC grade (food grade) and you may prefer FCF (furanocoumarin-free) from the plant *Citrus bergamia*

15 mL (1 Tablespoon) Alcohol*

40 Tea Bags or Loose Tea‡

1 <u>Glass</u> Jar - large enough to easily hold all of the tea bags.

Measure the Alcohol into the jar and add the Bergamot EO. Close the jar tightly and swirl until the mixture is blended and has coated the jar walls and lid. Remove the lid and allow the alcohol to slowly evaporate until no liquid pools at the bottom. You can replace the lid every ten minutes or so to swirl the mixture again.

Fill the jar with all of the teabags. You can use the tea right away, but it will develop a better flavor and aroma if you allow it to age for at least a week. Shake the jar every time you use the tea to allow tea in the center to be exposed to the jar's walls. Store the jar in a cool, dark place.

* When selecting alcohol, remember that it must be food grade, not from the pharmacy. To ensure this, insist upon *high proof* grain alcohol or neutral spirits from your liquor store. High proof is an indicator of the percentage of ethanol in the liquor. Divide any proof in half to find the percentage. 190 proof is 95% ethanol. 151 proof is 75% alcohol. For this recipe, 75% is the lowest recommended strength.

‡ The tea you choose can be green or black, decaffeinated or not, and you can even use Rooibos. For convenience, we prefer tea bags but you can use any loose tea or tisane variety. Tisane is a happy little French word that is pronounced like tea's on (teé-zon).

Monday 7

Arnold Crowther's Birthday

Tuesday 8

Draconids

Wednesday 9

Moon enters Pisces 11:06am

Thursday 10

1:28pm

Friday 11

Moon enters Aries 11:46pm

Saturday 12

Sunday 13

○ 4:09pm
Twi: 6:52am-Rise: 7:17am
Set: 6:43pm-Twi: 7:09pm

Communicating with a 3rd party may help. Wyrd luck around, be cunning.

Cimaruta, Charms of the Old Religion

The cimaruta (pronounced chee-mah-roó-tah) is a *composite charm*, meaning it is made from more than one charm. It is very old and comes from the folk traditions of Italy and Rome. Modern Italian-American Witches and practitioners of Italian Witchcraft known as Stregheria or Streghe, still wear these charms, as do some Dianic traditions. At one time the charm was hung over cribs to protect children, but now it is primarily used by modern Witches to **protect from baneful magic or spells and the Evil Eye.**

Its powerful protection properties are well known. The branch of the charm represents a sacred plant to Witches, rue - *Ruta graveolens*. Rue is used in many cultures to ward off the "Evil Eye" or negative envious energy projected by people that can cause harm.

The rue branches into three parts thought to represent the three phases of the Goddess. Each branch holds a symbol as part of this composite charm. Traditionally a crescent moon adorns one branch for Diana/Artemis, another branch has a key for Hekate, and the third branch holds a serpent for Proserpina/Persephone.

Other symbols vary by desire and design. The oldest symbols are a hand, a flower (always five-petaled and thought to be rose or vervain), a fish, horn, cock or eagle. Newer designs sometimes have a flaming heart, a later addition influenced by Christianity to represent Jesus. There are also designs that include all-seeing eyes, a sword, mano fico or mano cornuta (hands formed into protection gestures to avert the Evil Eye), mermaids, fish, and helmets.

The image on this page is an enhanced version of an illustration from *The Evil Eye* by Frederick Thomas Elworthy, 1895. Elworthy obtained the original charm for the illustration from a private collection held by a Mr. Neville Rolfe. In this design, the serpent wraps around the edge of the crescent moon.

Monday 14

Moon enters Taurus 11:24am
Patricia Crowther's Birthday
Federal holiday: Columbus Day

Tuesday 15

Wednesday 16

Moon enters Gemini 9:30pm
Dutch American Heritage Day

Thursday 17

Friday 18

Saturday 19

Moon enters Cancer 5:43am

Sunday 20

Moon Opposition Saturn
Selena Fox's Birthday
Twi: 6:58am-Rise: 7:23am
Set: 6:35pm-Twi: 7:00pm

Don't Panic

Basic Herbs & Oils for Witches

Over the years we have found several herbs, essential oils, and absolutes that we reach for constantly. This list of their magical correspondences only, but you will discover that every plant listed has medicinal properties and can be used to make healing potions.

All of these plants can be used in their dried form. Those marked with EO for Essential Oil and AB for Absolute are also excellent in their oil forms. The absolutes can be very costly, but the smallest amount of most absolutes will pack a powerful punch. For example, a single drop of jasmine absolute will scent over a quart (liter) of lotion!

Rosemary *Rosmarina officinalis* Mental stimulation, memory, study, mental acuity, healing; Excellent for purification! EO

Tea Tree *Melaleuca alternifolia* Strengthens will, healing and medicinal oil, used for cleansing and protection. Removes energy blocks, psychic gunk, "festering" energy, negative entities. EO

Atlas Cedar *Cedrus Atlantica* Manifesting, cleansing, protection, strength of will and courage EO

Rosemary

Citronella *Cymbopogon nardus* Clearing, uplifting, working with the Sun, repels insects. EO

Wintergreen *Gaultheria procumbens* Hex-breaking, counter-cursing, protection, healing EO

Star Anise *Illicium verum* Heightens psychic skills and aids their development, protection, purification, increased dreaming and dream recollection, helps in understanding interconnectedness EO

Opopanax *Commiphore erythrea* Acquiring knowledge and revealing what is hidden, protective (especially against psychic and magical drains), Divination, increased awareness, change EO

Spearmint *Mentha spicata* – Uplifting, protective while in deep states of consciousness and sleep, re-assuring, prosperity EO . . .

Monday 21

Orionids

◗ 7:40am
Moon enters Leo 11:29am

Tuesday 22

Orionids

Wednesday 23

Sun enters Scorpio 12:20pm
Moon enters Virgo 2:30pm

Thursday 24

United Nations Day

Friday 25

Moon enters Libra 3:20pm

Saturday 26

5:38am

Sunday 27

● 10:40pm
Moon enters Scorpio 3:30pm
Hindu: Diwali
Twi: 7:04am-Rise: 7:29am
Set: 6:27pm-Twi: 6:52pm

Celebrate, let loose! Use common sense to avoid troubles or litigation.

Pennyroyal *Mentha pulegium* Clears the mind, reduces marital tension, protects family and home, hex/curse breaking EO

Cinnamon/Cassia *Cinnamomum cassia* Luck, love and prosperity. A very useful oil for many purposes. Very popular for prosperity work and drawing beneficial people into your life. Used in many altar blends and all-purpose incense. EO

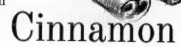

Cinnamon

Eucalyptus *Eucalyptus globulus* Very good for emotional balance and healing, especially after abuse. Calms chaos, disharmony, and conflict; healing. EO

Thyme *Thymus vulgaris* Improves other's perceptions of you and how you see yourself. Confidence, courage, increases loyalty. Strengthens personal fortitude and helps when grieving. Good for purification and cleansing for magical preparation. Some practitioners use thyme for prosperity and good luck. EO

Patchouli *Pogostemon cablin* Increases everything! Used as a catalyst to add energy to any purpose. Especially well suited to sensuality, love, lust, passion and related workings; prosperity, money. Helps manifest your magical intent in the 'real' world. EO

Jasmine *Jasminum grandiflorum* Attracts love, excellent for dream work and prophecy, balancing and soothing, reduces anxiety. Said to attract true love into your life. EO or AB

Rose *Rosa damascena and other species of the genus* All-around attraction, draws affection, love, friendship, luck, romance, opportunities. Good for psychic and magical powers, prophetic dreams, tuning-in to your personal power. EO or AB

Sandalwood *Santalum album and other species in the genus.* Treasured since antiquity for its exquisite fragrance and purifying properties. A very powerful, all-purpose oil for altars, anointing, spells, magic, rituals, blessing, protection, healing, charging,. . .

Monday 28

Tuesday 29

Moon enters Sagittarius 4:59pm

Wednesday 30

Thursday 31

☿ Retro
10:41am

🔯 Samhain Eve
🎃 Halloween

Friday 1

Moon in Capricorn
World Vegan Day

Day of the Dead
(Día de los Muertos)

Saturday 2

Sunday 3

Daylight Savings
Time Ends 2:00am
Moon enters Aquarius 5:20am

Twi: 6:10am-Rise: 6:36am
Set: 5:19pm-Twi: 5:46pm

November is Native
American Heritage Month

Great social opportunities to connect with friends and new ideas.

clearing. Raises spiritual vibrations, heightens awareness, opens psychic abilities. EO or AB

Mimosa *Acacia mearnsii* For dream recollection, increasing prophetic dreams, anti-hex and spell reversal, purification, amplifies personal power. EO or AB

Narcissus *Narcissus poeticus* Used for deepening dream states, calming the mind and spirit, peace & harmony. Also used for luck, especially in gambling. EO or AB

Sweet Violet - *Viola odorata*

Violet *viola odorata* Prosperity, attracting money, financial survival, protects against all baneful energy, connects with earth energies, good for changing your luck when things are down. EO or AB

Neroli *Citrus aurantium* Lifts the overall mood, increases energy and spiritual vibrations. Calming and peaceful while energetic. Brings positive energy, uplifting, also used for love and prosperity. EO/AB

Oil, Sachet & Infusion Recipes

If you do not have essential oils, you can use the dried plant materials in these recipes to make sachet charm bags (mojo bags) or to infuse into a carrier oil. The traditional apothecary abbreviations are used: gtt. and gtts. from gutta and guttae, Latin for drop(s). For larger amounts, milliliters are provided. 2.5 mL is about 49 drops. After you formulate your oils, be sure to dilute them before use. For a very strong concentrate, add the same amount of carrier oil as there are EO and AB combined. For example, when a recipe makes a teaspoon of oil, mix it with <u>at least</u> a teaspoon of carrier oil such as avocado, jojoba, olive or almond. . .

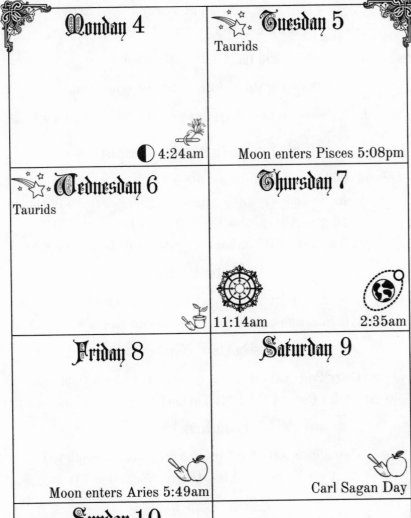

Monday 4

◐ 4:24am

Tuesday 5

Taurids

Moon enters Pisces 5:08pm

Wednesday 6

Taurids

Thursday 7

11:14am

2:35am

Friday 8

Moon enters Aries 5:49am

Saturday 9

Carl Sagan Day

Sunday 10

Islamic : Mawlid
(Prophet Muhammad's Birthday)

Moon enters Taurus 5:18pm
Twi: 6:16am-Rise: 6:42am
Set: 5:13pm-Twi: 5:40pm

Inner reflection and relaxation will get you back to your Witchy self.

Oil to Attract Friendship

3 gtts Rose AB | 20 gtts Sandalwood EO
1 gtt Cinnamon EO, 1 gtt Lavender EO

Oil for Lustful Attraction

Create the Oil of Attraction above and add:

1 gtt Patchouli EO | 1 gtt Jasmine AB | 1 gtt Violet AB

Oil for Purification & Banishing

This oil can be used in diffusers, diluted as a personal fragrance, or used to anoint doorways and window ledges to cleanse the home.

12 gtts Atlas Cedar EO | 10 gtts Clary Sage EO
1 gtt Rosemary EO | 2.5 mL (½ teaspoon) Sandalwood EO

Oil for Money

1 gtt Violet AB | 1 gtt Rose AB
3 gtts Spearmint | 2.5 mL (½ teaspoon) Sandalwood EO

Uncrossing Oil / Remove Hexes

3 gtts Clary Sage EO | 3 gtts Rosemary EO | 1 gtt Opopanax EO
20 gtts Atlas Cedar EO | 1 gtt Thyme | 10 gtts Frankincense EO

Good Luck Oil

1 gtt Violet AB | 1 gtt Rose AB | 1 gtt Patchouli EO
1 gtt Narcissus AB | 10 gtts Spearmint EO

Psychic Third-Eye Oil

1 gtt Rosemary EO| 10 gtts Frankincense EO | 1 gtt Star Anise EO
3 gtts Opopanax EO | 1 gtt Rose AB | 20 gtts Sandalwood EO
Add a very small nugget of Dragon's Blood resin to the bottle, a piece that would fit in a ⅛-¼ teaspoon measuring spoon.

Monday 11

Rare Transit of Mercury Across
the Sun (next occurence in 2039)
Excellent time for communication,
and starting new projects!
Federal Holiday: Veterans Day

Tuesday 12

◯ 7:36am

Wednesday 13

Moon enters Gemini 2:46am

Thursday 14

Friday 15

Moon enters Cancer 10:15am

Saturday 16

Moon Opposition Saturn

Sunday 17

Leonids

Moon enters Leo 3:57pm
Saturnalia begins
Israel Regardie's Birthday

Twi: 6:22am-Rrise: 6:49am
Set: 5:09pm-Twi: 5:35pm

Dispel depression and mother-like worries with gratitude meditations.

Lustral Baths

Witches use lustral baths prior to rituals, to prepare for magic, prior to initiation, or to purify for any purposes. It is a cleansing and purification of mind, body, spirit, aura, soul. . . essentially the entire person. They remove hexes and help you tune into your "Witchy" self before you enter into a magical circle or cast a spell.

Lustral refers to ceremonial purification, especially in consecrated waters. The term was first used in the 1530s and comes from Latin *lustralis* and *lustrum*. A lustrum is a period of five years. Lustrum was originally a purification sacrifice performed every five years after the quinquennial census. Lustral developed from this word however, it now refers to just the purification ritual.

Draw yourself a nice warm bath. Place a few candles around, light some incense and set the mood. Focus your mind and add three small handfuls of sea salt. As you add each handful of salt you are consecrating it while cleansing the bath water, purifying it and setting it aside for this specific purpose. This is no different than making Holy Water, you are simply making a lot of it. Visualize your energy flowing through your body, down your arm, into your hand, into the salt, and then into the water as you add each handful. For each salt addition, use Words of Power of your own design, or say:

1st Handful: *Clear of mind and pure of heart,*
This time and place is set apart.
2nd Handful: *Banish bane and purify,*
Negativity I defy.
3rd Handful: *Blessed salt and purified water,*
I become the sacred altar

To seal the work, you can say *I hereby consecrate this salt and cleanse this water*, or simply *say so mote it be.*

Monday 18
Leonids

Tuesday 19

◐ 3:12pm
Moon enters Virgo 7:55pm

Wednesday 20
☿ Direct
1:12pm

Transgender Day of Remembrance

Thursday 21

Moon enters Libra 10:20pm

Friday 22

Sun enters Sagittarius 8:59am

Saturday 23
1:40am

Moon enters Scorpio 11:59pm
Saturnalia ends

Sunday 24

Look West just after Sunset to see
the Conjunction of Venus & Jupiter
Twi: 6:29am-Rise: 6:56am
Set: 5:05pm-Twi: 5:32pm

Those who enjoy debate will challenge your communication skills.

Lunar-Lustral Baths

A lunar-lustral bath is a wonderful way to prepare for rituals on the full moon and it can be your primary Esbat ritual in itself. Lunar energy is excellent for boosting your personal energy. Magical and psychic powers flow more freely after a moon bath, and they are helpful for detoxing your body.

Like other lustral baths, lunar-lustral baths are purifying and will cleanse the psychic junk and negativity from you.

Set the mood by lowering the lights or by lighting a few candles. Burn some incense or use an essential oil diffuser to fragrance the air. Scents of plants associated with the moon are great choices. Try sandalwood, myrrh, jasmine, gardenia, or lily. If you can see the moon outside of your bathroom window open the curtains and let the moonlight filter in. Do what makes you feel the most comfortable.

Before adding your salt to the water as described last week, infuse the salt with your choice of oil attuned to the moon. Put the salt in a bowl and drop the oils into the middle of the salt. Use the back of a spoon to crush and mix the oil into the salt until it is completely coated. See the Lunar Bath Salts recipe below.

Once you are in the bath, relax and perform any visualizations you normally use to detox and energize. Close your eyes, breath deeply, say any Words of Power of your choice.

Lunar Bath Salts

½ cup Sea Salt
3 drops Jasmine AB*

*Alternate Choices: 3 drops Gardenia AB, ½ teaspoon Sandalwood EO, 3 drops Star Anise EO, 3 drops Sage EO, 3 drops Clary Sage EO, 1 drop Chamomile EO, 3 drops Juniper EO, 3 drops Mugwort

Monday 25

Tuesday 26

● 9:07am
Moon enters Sagittarius 2:11am

Wednesday 27

Thursday 28

Look for Mercury low in
the East just before Sunrise

Moon enters Capricorn 6:33am
Federal Holiday: Thanksgiving

Friday 29

Saturday 30

Moon enters Aquarius 2:14pm
Austin Osman Spare's Birthday
Oberon Zell-Ravenheart's Birthday

Sunday 1

Twi: 6:35am-Rise: 7:02am
Set: 5:03pm-Twi: 5:31pm

On December 1, 2007: The first
military grave marker with a pentacle
allowed for military veterans.

Solitude now gives you insight before the upcoming hustle and bustle.

The "Real" Book of Shadows

A Book of Shadows (BoS) is a personal book of spells, recipes, journal entries, charts, and more; much like this almanac. There is no 'original' BoS from ancient times, and a BoS is not holy writ.

Each BoS is unique to the individual practitioner. Covens will occasionally share a single BoS, or each coven member may copy out of a 'master' coven BoS and add their own work to their individual books. Many covens within a single tradition may also share a 'master' BoS which contains by-laws and tax-exempt church information. However, even when a tradition has a 'master' BoS, it is normal for each individual to have a personal BoS.

When a coven does have a 'master' BoS, it is normal for the High Priestess or High Priest (HP/s) to house the book. In these formal coven structures, new initiates are allowed to copy sections of the 'master' BoS into their own personal books. There are a growing number of covens without a hierarchical structure, and each member takes turns directing rituals as an HP/s would. In these instances, every member keeps a BoS and they contain both personal records and coven documents and rituals.

It is extremely unlikely that there was ever a 'true original Book of Shadows'. Like most folk traditions and religions, teachings were passed on orally and sometimes developed into myths and fairy tales.

There are some famous Books of Shadows, such as Gerald B. Gardner's, which contains reconstructed rituals including information from many sources such as The Greater Key of Solomon, Freemasonry, the Golden Dawn, Robert Graves, Charles Leland, Aleister Crowley, etc.

Your own BoS can be anything you like. It should serve your needs as you change and grow. For this reason, a spell-binder is highly recommended. Learn about spell-binders next week.

Monday 2

Tuesday 3

Moon enters Pisces 1:11am

Wednesday 4

10:08pm 1:00am

Thursday 5

Moon enters Aries 1:45pm
World Soil Day

Friday 6

Saturday 7

Sunday 8

Moon enters Taurus 1:30am

Twi: 6:40am-Rise: 7:08am
Set: 5:03pm-Twi: 5:31pm

Set goals, ground, and follow routines.

The Spell Binder

People change, and because your Book of Shadows is a direct reflection of you and your practice, it will constantly change too. Rather than purchasing an expensive leather or cloth-bound tome in which to carefully calligraphy and illuminate, it is easier to use the more flexible version, a binder.

With a spell-binder, you can pull out pages and replace them when you make a mistake. It is possible to rearrange pages and binders are infinitely expandable. You can use different colored pages for organizational purposes or magical color correspondences, and you can even use black paper with the milky white or silver gel pens to write in reverse of normal. This is fun to do for moonlight and candlelight rituals as the reflective text is easier to read in such lighting.

Three-ring binders can be found easily, and luxurious models are available. Look for presentation binders or post-style scrapbooks that hold standard size paper in protective sleeves.

You can use several spellbinders for various purposes. For recipes, top-loading sheet protectors will save you heartache. These are thin plastic envelopes that fit into your binder. For moonlight and candlelight work, it is easier to read through the anti-glare matte or satin-finish protectors rather than the shiny ones.

If you like to collect spells, you can print them out in fancy fonts and add them to your Book of Shadows easily. When you copy something, always quote your sources. If you are printing out web pages, be sure that the URL (link) appears on the printed page, and note the author. Anything taken from books, magazines, newspapers, etc. should also have the source and author noted. Remember that you can use the works of other authors for your own individual personal use, but cannot distribute them such as by putting them on a website or passing them out to your friends.

Monday 9

Tuesday 10

Moon enters Gemini 10:47am

Wednesday 11

◯11:13pm

Thursday 12

Moon enters Cancer 5:23pm

Frank Sinatra's Birthday

Friday 13

Geminids

Saturday 14

Geminids

Moon Opposition Saturn

Moon enters Leo 9:56pm

Sunday 15

Friday Gladheart's Birthday

Twi: 6:45am-Rise: 7:13am

Set: 5:04pm-Twi: 5:32pm

Friends and family come through for you.

Earth, Air, Fire, Water

Earth

The Earth element symbolizes substance, matter, foundations, survival, practicality, responsibility, fertility, grounding, and the manifestation of matter. Earth is often seen as a feminine element although all polarities are contained within each element. Magic involving images, knots and cords, gardens, crystals, and stones is generally categorized as Earth magic.

Air

The element of Air symbolizes communication, birth, rebirth, the spoken word, thoughts, ideas, and the manifestation of thoughts. Air is often seen as a masculine element, although again all polarities are contained within each element. Magic involving Words of Power and visualization generally fall under the category of Air magic. Some forms of divination magic also fall under the Air category.

Fire

The Fire element symbolizes change, transformation, purification, sensuality, sexuality, passion, and manifestation of change. Fire is often viewed as a masculine element. Magic involving candles, fires, and many healing workings fall under the category of Fire magic.

Water

The element of water symbolizes emotions, cycles (particularly the cycle of purification brought about by birth, death, and rebirth), and the manifestation of emotions. Water is often seen as a. . .

Monday 16

Tuesday 17

Moon enters Virgo 1:16am

Wednesday 18

2:25pm   ◑ 10:58pm

Thursday 19

Ronald Hutton's Birthday
Moon enters Libra 4:05am

Friday 20

Saturday 21

Sun enters Capricorn 10:19pm

Ursids

Solstice

10:19pm   Moon enters Scorpio 6:58am

Sunday 22

Ursids

Jewish: Hanukkah begins
Twi: 6:49am-Rise: 7:17am
Set: 5:07pm-Twi: 5:35pm

Moving forward towards brighter horizons.

feminine element. Magic involving mirrors, baths, some forms of divination, and weather magic (when precipitation is the goal) generally fall under the category of Water magic.

The Fifth Element

The fifth element goes by many names; Center, Ether, Æthyr, Akasha (in Hindu Sankhya philosophy), the higher self, Spirit, and more. The pentacle is used most often to represent this element because each point on the star can be seen as one of the four elements with the top point being the fifth. This element represents the synthesis* and manifestation* of all elements. The fifth element unifies and transcends the other four elements. It is synergistic, meaning that its total effect is greater than the sum of the individual elements.

Manifestation

the act or process of something becoming 'real' in the mundane. If something were to 'manifest' it would mean it is becoming evident, certain, and perceivable. An accounting plan may manifest itself in the increasing success of a business. A spell may manifest itself as physical results, these physical results can be termed manifestations.

Synthesis

Synthesis comes to us from the Greek word *syntithenai* which means to put together, the combining or uniting of many parts to make a whole.

Monday 23

Moon enters Sagittarius 10:35am

Tuesday 24

Wednesday 25

● 11:14pm
☾ 11:18pm - Annular, not visible
Christian: Christmas

Thursday 26

Kwanzaa begins

Friday 27

Moon enters Aquarius 11:21pm

Saturday 28

Sunday 29

Twi: 6:52am-Rise: 7:20am
Set: 5:11pm-Twi: 5:39pm

A very lucky week! Happiness, friends, joy, family and contentment.

(Message written in Theban Script)

Theban-script paragraph (six lines) followed by:

⟨Theban word⟩: 2019
⟨Theban word⟩: ⟨Theban word⟩-⟨Theban word⟩
(all lower case)

Thank you from the PW team!

Bruce A. Grayson   *R. Jensen*   *Friday Gladheart*
Almanac@PracticalWitch.com

Theban Script

ꟾ						
A	B	C	D	E	F	G
H	I & J	K	L	M	N	
O	P	Q	R	S	T	
U & V	W	X	Y	Z		

Monday 30

Moon enters Pisces 9:42am
Jewish: Hanukkah ends

Tuesday 31

Wednesday 1

Moon enters
Aries 10:01pm   7:30 pm
Kwanzaa ends
Federal Holiday: New Year's Day

Thursday 2

◑ 10:47pm

Friday 3

Saturday 4

Moon enters Taurus 10:16am
World Braille Day:
Jason Mankey's Birthday
Doreen Valiente's Birthday
Isaac Newton's Birthday

Sunday 5

Perihelion: 1:47 am, Earth is
closest to the Sun in orbit.
Twi: 6:54am-Rise: 7:22am
Set: 5:16pm-Twi: 5:44pm

Review your year; look how far you have come!

2020

January

Mo	Tu	We	Th	Fr	Sa	Su
		1	2	3	4	5
6	7	8	9	10	11	12
13	14	15	16	17	18	19
20	21	22	23	24	25	26
27	28	29	30	31		

2:◑ 10:○ 17:◑ 24:●

February

Mo	Tu	We	Th	Fr	Sa	Su
					1	2
3	4	5	6	7	8	9
10	11	12	13	14	15	16
17	18	19	20	21	22	23
24	25	26	27	28	29	

1:◑ 9:○ 15:◑ 23:●

March

Mo	Tu	We	Th	Fr	Sa	Su
						1
2	3	4	5	6	7	8
9	10	11	12	13	14	15
16	17	18	19	20	21	22
23	24	25	26	27	28	29
30	31					

2:◑ 9:○ 16:◑ 24:●

April

Mo	Tu	We	Th	Fr	Sa	Su
		1	2	3	4	5
6	7	8	9	10	11	12
13	14	15	16	17	18	19
20	21	22	23	24	25	26
27	28	29	30			

1:◑ 7:○ 14:◑ 22:● 30:◑

May

Mo	Tu	We	Th	Fr	Sa	Su
				1	2	3
4	5	6	7	8	9	10
11	12	13	14	15	16	17
18	19	20	21	22	23	24
25	26	27	28	29	30	31

7:○ 14:◑ 22:● 29:◑

June

Mo	Tu	We	Th	Fr	Sa	Su
1	2	3	4	5	6	7
8	9	10	11	12	13	14
15	16	17	18	19	20	21
22	23	24	25	26	27	28
29	30					

5:○ 13:◑ 21:● 28:◑

July

Mo	Tu	We	Th	Fr	Sa	Su
		1	2	3	4	5
6	7	8	9	10	11	12
13	14	15	16	17	18	19
20	21	22	23	24	25	26
27	28	29	30	31		

4:○ 12:◑ 20:● 27:◑

August

Mo	Tu	We	Th	Fr	Sa	Su
					1	2
3	4	5	6	7	8	9
10	11	12	13	14	15	16
17	18	19	20	21	22	23
24	25	26	27	28	29	30
31						

3:○ 11:◑ 18:● 25:◑

September

Mo	Tu	We	Th	Fr	Sa	Su
	1	2	3	4	5	6
7	8	9	10	11	12	13
14	15	16	17	18	19	20
21	22	23	24	25	26	27
28	29	30				

2:○ 10:◑ 17:● 23:◑

October

Mo	Tu	We	Th	Fr	Sa	Su
			1	2	3	4
5	6	7	8	9	10	11
12	13	14	15	16	17	18
19	20	21	22	23	24	25
26	27	28	29	30	31	

1:○ 9:◑ 16:● 23:◑ 31:○

November

Mo	Tu	We	Th	Fr	Sa	Su
						1
2	3	4	5	6	7	8
9	10	11	12	13	14	15
16	17	18	19	20	21	22
23	24	25	26	27	28	29
30						

8:◑ 14:● 21:◑ 30:○

December

Mo	Tu	We	Th	Fr	Sa	Su
	1	2	3	4	5	6
7	8	9	10	11	12	13
14	15	16	17	18	19	20
21	22	23	24	25	26	27
28	29	30	31			

7:◑ 14:● 21:◑ 29:○

Measurement Abbreviations & Equivalents

gtt/gtts - drop or drops

tsp. - teaspoon

T./Tbl. - Tablespoon

oz. - ounce

2.5 mL = ½ teaspoon

49 drops in ½ teaspoon

2 Tbl. = 1 ounce

mL - milliliter   g. - gram

Credits & References

Several individuals have helped to create this Almanac, and our gratitude goes to Bruce A. Grayson for his crucial editorial input. All graphics, energy notes, article content and editing provided by the team at Practical Witch. Visit the site to read about these contributors. All astronomical events are derived by referencing and cross checking numerous sources for the greatest accuracy:

- U.S. Naval Observatory Database
- Jet Propulsion Laboratory Development Ephemeris: JPL DE430 from Pasadena, California
- The Swiss Ephemeris: a highly precise ephemeris developed by Astrodienst, largely based on NASA's JPL DE431, released 9/2013.
- Moon phases, sun and moon times cross checked to longitude & latitude with Daff Moon Version 2.8 Copyright 2017 Evgeny Fedorischenk
- Meteor showers verification from: American Meteor Society Ephemeris
- Sunrise and set time verification from: the ChronosXP 4.1 program, version 4.1, developed by Robert Misiak
- Chinese New Year information from: Chinese Fortune Calendar, Travel China Guide and Time and Date AS 1995–2017.
- Moon Signs: The American Ephemeris for the 20th/21st Century by Neil F. Michelsen
- Exact cross quarter Sabbat dates are based on the more precise spacial method rather than splitting time intervals between Solstices and Equinoxes. They are interpolated as the midway points between the Solstices and Equinoxes measured in degrees along the ecliptic by former NASA scientist Rollin Gillespie as provided on the Archaeo Astronomy website
- Exact cross quarters verified through various ephemeris and the work of Arnold Barmettler. ~30~

Notes

Notes

Notes

Notes

Notes

Notes

SUBSCRIBE TO EVERYTHING WE PUBLISH!

Do you love what Microcosm publishes?

Do you want us to publish more great stuff?

Would you like to receive each new title as it's published?

Subscribe as a BFF to our new titles and we'll mail them all to you as they are released!

$10-30/mo, pay what you can afford. Include your t-shirt size and your birthday for a possible surprise!

microcosmpublishing.com/bff

...AND HELP US GROW YOUR SMALL WORLD!